# CONTENTS

How to use this book

NVQ competences

## workbook activities

| | | |
|---|---|---|
| 1 | The accounting system | 2 |
| 2 | Double-entry book-keeping | 5 |
| 3 | Balancing accounts and the trial balance | 9 |
| 4 | Final accounts – the extended trial balance | 14 |
| 5 | Accruals and prepayments | 18 |
| 6 | Depreciation of fixed assets | 22 |
| 7 | Bad debts and provision for bad debts | 26 |
| 8 | The regulatory framework of accounting | 32 |
| 9 | Control accounts | 36 |
| 10 | The journal – correction of errors | 41 |
| 11 | Bank reconciliation statements | 44 |
| 12 | Incomplete records | 47 |
| 13 | Club and society accounts | 56 |
| 14 | Partnership accounts | 60 |
| 15 | Manufacturing accounts | 64 |
| 16 | Accounting for capital transactions | 67 |

## assignments

| | | |
|---|---|---|
| 1 | James Belushi – incomplete records | 71 |
| 2 | Andy Gillman – extended trial balance | 80 |

3   Adcock & Tweed
    – accruals, prepayments and club accounts              87

4   Hillview Leisure
    – dealing with capital transactions                    98

5   Marston & Banks
    – manufacturing accounts and partnerships             114

6   Bon Voyage Limited
    – bank reconciliations and control accounts           123

## simulations

1   Branson & Company                                     133

2   Harvey & Company                                      161

3   Cooper & Mason                                        175

## central assessment tasks

1   Creative Catering                                     187

2   Colin Drew                                            199

3   Electronics World Limited                             211

4   Castle Alarms                                         223

## appendix – photocopiable documents

235

# FINANCIAL
# *Accounting*

## workbook

## NVQ LEVEL 3
## ACCOUNTING

David Cox,
with contributions by Derek Street

OSBORNE BOOKS

Published by Osborne Books Limited
Unit 1B Everoak Estate
Bromyard Road
Worcester
WR2 5HN
Tel 01905 748071
Email books@osbornebooks.co.uk
www.osbornebooks.co.uk


Printed by the Bath Press, Bath.


British Library Cataloguing in Publication Data
A catalogue record for this book is available from the British Library


ISBN 1 872962 43 2

# ACKNOWLEDGEMENTS

The author wishes to thank the following for their help with the compilation, reading and production of the text of this book: Angela Davis, Catherine Fardon, Michael Fardon, Robert Fardon, Michael Gilbert, Rosemarie Griffiths and Jon Moore. Thanks are also due to Anita Sherwood of Hedgehog for the graphic designs on the cover and within the text.

Particular thanks go to Derek Street for contributing assignments and simulations and to Roger Petheram for reading the text, commenting upon it and for carrying out the unenviable task of checking the answers.

Osborne Books is greatly indebted to the Association of Accounting Technicians for their generous help and advice and permission to reproduce a sample simulation and Central Assessments and also to the Lead Body for Accounting for permission to reproduce extracts from the Standards of Competence for Accounting.

# HOW TO USE THIS BOOK

*Financial Accounting Workbook* is designed to be used alongside Osborne Books' *Financial Accounting Tutorial* and is ideal for student use in the classroom, at home and on distance learning courses.

*Financial Accounting Workbook* is divided into four sections: workbook activities, assignments, simulations and Central Assessment tasks.

### workbook activities

Workbook activities are self-contained exercises which are designed to be used to supplement the activities in the tutorial text. Many of them are more extended than the exercises in *Financial Accounting Tutorial* and provide useful practice for students preparing for simulations. Some of the activities involve the completion of documents and forms such as ledger accounts, journals, extended trial balances and asset registers. These are reproduced in photocopiable form within the Appendix at the back of the book.

### assignments

These are self-contained sets of activities which extend learning further and provide useful practice for the simulations which follow. Many of the documents and forms needed for the assignments are printed within the text and may be written in as required. Alternatively the Appendix may be photocopied and the appropriate documents and forms extracted.

### simulations

There are three full-length simulations in this workbook. The first has been produced by AAT and is reproduced with their kind permission. The other two simulations have been newly written for this workbook. Again, many of the documents and forms needed for the assignments are printed within the text and may be written in as required.

### Central Assessment tasks

Osborne Books is grateful to AAT for their kind permission to reproduce the material in this section. The tasks for each Central Assessment are set out consecutively, because the material is inter-dependent and cross-referenced. The tasks, however, may be carried out on separate occasions, and do not necessarily have to be time constrained.

### answers

Answers are not provided in the text. A Tutor Pack is available separately. Please telephone Osborne Books on 01905 748071 for details.

# NVQ COMPETENCES

## UNIT 5 (previously Unit 4): MAINTAINING FINANCIAL RECORDS AND PREPARING ACCOUNTS

### element 1

### maintain records relating to capital acquisition and disposal

❏ *relevant details relating to capital expenditure are correctly entered in the appropriate records*

❏ *the organisation's records agree with the physical presence of capital items*

❏ *all acquisition and disposal costs and revenues are correctly identified and recorded in the appropriate records*

❏ *depreciation charges and other necessary entries and adjustments are correctly calculated and recorded in the appropriate records*

❏ *the records clearly show the prior authority for capital expenditure and disposal and indicate the approved method of funding and disposal*

❏ *profit and loss on disposal is correctly calculated and recorded in the appropriate records*

❏ *the organisation's policies and procedures relating to the maintenance of capital records are adhered to*

❏ *lack of agreement between physical items and records are identified and either resolved or referred to the appropriate person*

❏ *when possible, suggestions for improvements in the way the organisation maintains its capital records are made to the appropriate person*

### element 2

### record income and expenditure

❏ *all income and expenditure is correctly identified and recorded in the appropriate records*

❏ *relevant accrued and prepaid income and expenditure is correctly identified and adjustments are made*

❏ *the organisation's policies, regulations, procedures and timescales in relation to recording income and expenditure are observed*

❏ *incomplete data is identified and either resolved or referred to the appropriate person*

## element 3

### collect and collate information for the preparation of final accounts

❏ *relevant accounts and reconciliations are correctly prepared to allow the preparation of final accounts*

❏ *all relevant information is correctly identified and recorded*

❏ *investigations into business transactions are conducted with tact and courtesy*

❏ *the organisation's policies, regulations, procedures and timescales relating to preparing final accounts are observed*

❏ *discrepancies and unusual features are identified and either resolved or referred to the appropriate person*

❏ *the trial balance is accurately prepared and, where necessary, a suspense account is opened and reconciled*

## element 4

### prepare the extended trial balance

❏ *totals from the general ledger or other records are correctly entered on the extended trial balance*

❏ *material errors disclosed by the trial balance are identified, traced and referred to the appropriate authority*

❏ *adjustments not dealt with in the ledger accounts are correctly entered on the extended trial balan*

❏ *an agreed valuation of closing stock is correctly entered on the extended trial balance*

❏ *the organisation's policies, regulations, procedures and timescales in relation to preparing extended trial balances are observed*

❏ *discrepancies, unusual features or queries are identified and either resolved or referred to the appropriate person*

❏ *the extended trial balance is accurately extended and totalled*

## coverage of NVQ specifications

The Osborne Books *Financial Accounting Tutorial* and *Financial Accounting Workbook* between them cover the performance criteria set out above. For coverage of the performance criteria by individual chapters, please see the introductory pages of the tutorial text.

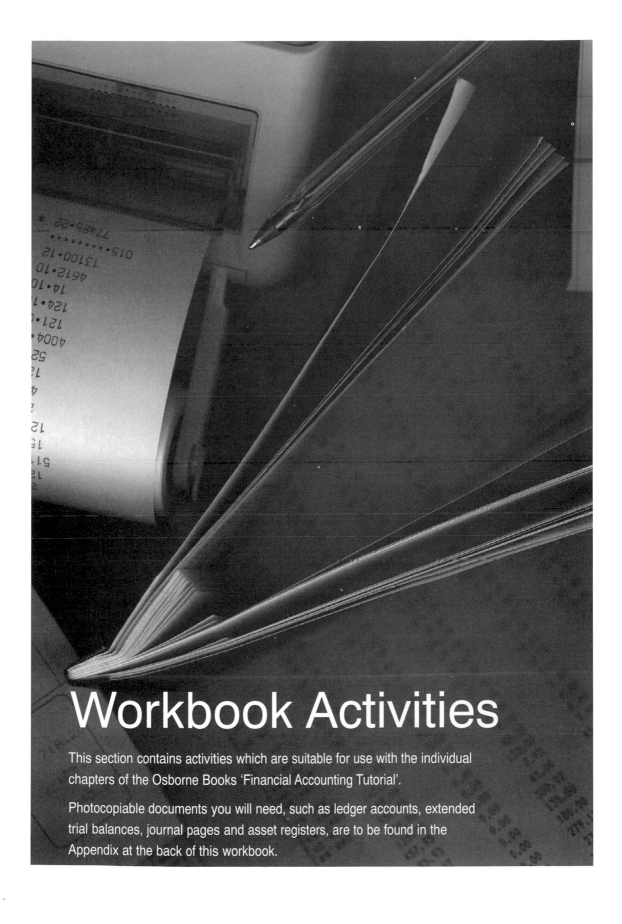

# Workbook Activities

This section contains activities which are suitable for use with the individual chapters of the Osborne Books 'Financial Accounting Tutorial'.

Photocopiable documents you will need, such as ledger accounts, extended trial balances, journal pages and asset registers, are to be found in the Appendix at the back of this workbook.

# 1 THE ACCOUNTING SYSTEM

**1.1** Write out and complete the following:

(a) The ..................................... accountant is mainly concerned with external reporting.

(b) The sales day book is an example of a ...............................  ............................... record.

(c) Sales ledger contains the personal accounts of ........................................

(d) Sales account is contained in the .................................................. ledger.

(e) Income minus ..................................... equals ...........................................

(f) .......................................... minus ...................................... equals capital.

**1.2** In an accounting system, which one of the following represents the most logical sequence?

(a) primary accounting record; prime documents; double-entry book-keeping; trial balance; final accounts

(b) prime documents; primary accounting records; double-entry book-keeping; trial balance; final accounts

(c) prime documents; primary accounting records; double-entry book-keeping; final accounts; trial balance

(d) prime documents; double-entry book-keeping, primary accounting records; trial balance; final accounts

Answer (a) or (b) or (c) or (d)

**1.3** Write out the figures which make up the accounting equation (assets – liabilities = capital) after each of the following consecutive transactions (ignore VAT):

- owner starts in business with capital of £10,000 comprising £9,000 in the bank and £1,000 in cash

- buys office equipment for £2,500, paying by cheque

- obtains a loan of £2,000 by cheque from a friend

- buys factory machinery for £8,000, paying by cheque

- buys office equipment for £2,000 on credit from Wyvern Office Supplies

**1.4** Fill in the missing figures:

|     | Assets<br>£ | Liabilities<br>£ | Capital<br>£ |
|-----|-------------|------------------|--------------|
| (a) | 10,000 | 0 | .......... |
| (h) | 20,000 | 7,500 | .......... |
| (c) | 16,750 | .......... | 10,500 |
| (d) | .......... | 4,350 | 12,680 |
| (e) | 17,290 | .......... | 11,865 |
| (f) | .......... | 6,709 | 17,294 |

**1.5**   The table below sets out account balances from the books of a business. The columns (a) to (f) show the account balances resulting from a series of transactions that have taken place over time. You are to compare each set of adjacent columns, ie (a) with (b) with (c), and so on, and state, with figures, what accounting transactions have taken place in each case. (Ignore VAT).

|  | (a) | (b) | (c) | (d) | (e) | (f) |
|---|---|---|---|---|---|---|
|  | £ | £ | £ | £ | £ | £ |
| **Assets** | | | | | | |
| Office equipment | – | 5,000 | 5,000 | 5,500 | 5,500 | 5,500 |
| Machinery | – | – | – | – | 6,000 | 6,000 |
| Bank | 7,000 | 2,000 | 7,000 | 7,000 | 1,000 | 3,000 |
| Cash | 1,000 | 1,000 | 1,000 | 500 | 500 | 500 |
| **Liabilities** | | | | | | |
| Loan | – | – | 5,000 | 5,000 | 5,000 | 5,000 |
| **Capital** | 8,000 | 8,000 | 8,000 | 8,000 | 8,000 | 10,000 |

Note: a set of photocopiable blank ledger
accounts is printed in the Appendix.

# 2 DOUBLE-ENTRY BOOK-KEEPING

**2.1** Fill in the missing words to the following sentences:

(a) A ........................... entry records an account which gains value, or records an asset, or an expense.

(b) In the books of a business, the ........................... side of bank account records money paid out.

(c) In capital account, the initial capital contributed by the owner of the business is recorded on the ........................... side.

(d) Office equipment is an example of a ........................... asset.

(e) The purchase of a photocopier for use in the office is classed as ........................... expenditure.

(f) Repairs to a photocopier are classed as ........................... expenditure.

**2.2** The following are the business transactions of Andrew King (who is not registered for VAT) for the month of October 1999:

| | |
|---|---|
| 1 Oct | Started in business with capital of £7,500 in the bank |
| 4 Oct | Bought a machine for £4,000, paying by cheque |
| 6 Oct | Bought office equipment for £2,250, paying by cheque |
| 11 Oct | Paid rent £400, by cheque |
| 12 Oct | Obtained a loan of £1,500 from a friend, Tina Richards, and paid her cheque into the bank |
| 15 Oct | Paid wages £500, by cheque |
| 18 Oct | Commission received £200, by cheque |
| 20 Oct | Drawings £250, by cheque |
| 25 Oct | Paid wages £450, by cheque |

**You are to:**

(a) write up Andrew King's bank account

(b) complete the double-entry book-keeping transactions

**2.3**   Write short notes, distinguishing between:

    (a)   capital expenditure and revenue expenditure

    (b)   debit balance and credit balance

    (c)   bank account and cash account

    (d)   capital account and drawings account

**2.4**   The purchase of goods for resale on credit is recorded in the accounts as:

|     | *Debit* | *Credit* |
|-----|---------|----------|
| (a) | creditor's account | purchases account |
| (b) | purchases account | cash account |
| (c) | purchases account | creditor's account |
| (d) | creditor's account | sales account |

Answer (a) or (b) or (c) or (d)

**2.5**   Unsatisfactory goods, which were purchased on credit, are returned to the supplier. This is recorded in the accounts as:

|     | *Debit* | *Credit* |
|-----|---------|----------|
| (a) | sales returns account | creditor's account |
| (b) | purchases returns account | creditor's account |
| (c) | creditor's account | purchases returns account |
| (d) | creditor's account | purchases account |

Answer (a) or (b) or (c) or (d)

**2.6**   Write short notes, distinguishing between:

    (a)   cash purchases and credit purchases

    (b)   sales and sales returns

    (c)   carriage inwards and carriage outwards

    (d)   discount allowed and discount received

**2.7**   For each transaction below, complete the table to show the accounts which will be debited and credited:

(a)   Bought goods, paying by cheque

(b)   Cheque received for cash sales

(c)   Bought goods on credit from Teme Traders

(d)   Sold goods on credit to L Harris

(e)   Returned unsatisfactory goods to Teme Traders

(f)   L Harris returns unsatisfactory goods

(g)   Received a loan from D Perkins, by cheque

(h)   Withdrew cash from the bank for use in the business

| Transaction | Account debited | Account credited |
|---|---|---|
| (a) | | |
| (b) | | |
| (c) | | |
| (d) | | |
| (e) | | |
| (f) | | |
| (g) | | |
| (h) | | |

*Note: ignore Value Added Tax*

**2.8**    The following are the business transactions of Pershore Packaging for the month of January 1999:

| | |
|---|---|
| 4 Jan | Bought goods, £250, on credit from AB Supplies Limited |
| 5 Jan | Sold goods, £195, a cheque being received |
| 7 Jan | Sold goods, £150, cash being received |
| 11 Jan | Received a loan of £1,000 from J Johnson by cheque |
| 15 Jan | Paid £250 to AB Supplies Limited by cheque |
| 18 Jan | Sold goods, £145, on credit to L Lewis |
| 20 Jan | Bought goods, £225, paying by cheque |
| 22 Jan | Paid wages, £125, in cash |
| 26 Jan | Bought office equipment, £160, on credit from Mercia Office Supplies Limited |
| 28 Jan | Received a cheque for £145 from L Lewis |
| 29 Jan | Paid the amount owing to Mercia Office Supplies Limited by cheque |

**You are to** record the transactions in the books of account.

*Notes:*

•    *Pershore Packaging is not registered for Value Added Tax*

•    *day books are not required*


**2.9**    Enter the following transactions into the double-entry accounts of Sonya Smith:

1999

| | |
|---|---|
| 2 Feb | Bought goods £200, on credit from G Lewis |
| 4 Feb | Sold goods £150, on credit to L Jarvis |
| 8 Feb | Sold goods £240, on credit to G Patel |
| 10 Feb | Paid G Lewis the amount owing by cheque after deducting a cash discount of 5% |
| 12 Feb | L Jarvis pays the amount owing by cheque after deducting a cash discount of 2% |
| 17 Feb | Bought goods £160, on credit from G Lewis |
| 19 Feb | G Patel pays the amount owing by cheque after deducting a cash discount of 2.5% |
| 24 Feb | Paid G Lewis the amount owing by cheque after deducting a cash discount of 5% |

*Notes:*

•    *Sonya Smith is not registered for Value Added Tax*

•    *day books are not required*

Note: a set of photocopiable blank ledger accounts is printed in the Appendix.

# 3 BALANCING ACCOUNTS AND THE TRIAL BALANCE

**3.1**   Which one of the following accounts normally has a debit balance?

(a)   loan

(b)   bank overdraft

(c)   sales

(d)   purchases

Answer (a) or (b) or (c) or (d)

**3.2**   Which one of the following accounts normally has a credit balance?

(a)   drawings

(b)   capital

(c)   cash

(d)   premises

Answer (a) or (b) or (c) or (d)

**3.3**   Produce the trial balance of Tina Wong as at 30 November 1999. She has omitted to open a capital account.

|  | £ |
|---|---|
| Bank overdraft | 1,855 |
| Purchases | 2,419 |
| Cash | 85 |
| Sales | 4,164 |
| Purchases returns | 102 |
| Creditors | 1,082 |
| Equipment | 2,500 |
| Van | 7,500 |
| Sales returns | 354 |
| Debtors | 2,115 |
| Wages | 1,230 |
| Capital | ? |

**3.4** The book-keeper of Lorna Fox has extracted the following list of balances as at 31 March 1999:

|  | £ |
|---|---|
| Purchases | 96,250 |
| Sales | 146,390 |
| Sales returns | 8,500 |
| Administration expenses | 10,240 |
| Wages | 28,980 |
| Telephone | 3,020 |
| Interest paid | 2,350 |
| Travel expenses | 1,045 |
| Premises | 125,000 |
| Machinery | 40,000 |
| Debtors | 10,390 |
| Bank overdraft | 1,050 |
| Cash | 150 |
| Creditors | 10,545 |
| Value Added Tax (amount due) | 1,950 |
| Loan from bank | 20,000 |
| Drawings | 9,450 |
| Capital | 155,440 |

**You are to:**

(a) Produce the trial balance at 31 March 1999.

(b) Take any three debit balances and any three credit balances and explain to someone who does not understand accounting why they are listed as such, and what this means to the business.

**3.5**   Fill in the missing words from the following sentences:

(a)   "You made an error of ........................................................ when you debited the cost of diesel

fuel for the van to Vans Account."

(b)   "I've had the book-keeper from D Jones Limited on the 'phone concerning the statements of

account that we sent out the other day. She says that there is a sales invoice charged that

she knows nothing about. I wonder if we have done a ...................................... and it should

be for T Jones' account?"

(c)   "There is a 'bad figure' on a purchases invoice – we have read it as £35 when it should be

£55. It has gone through our accounts wrongly so we have an error of ..........................

.......................... to put right."

(d)   "Although the trial balance balanced last week, I've since found an error of £100 in the

calculation of the balance of sales account. We will need to check the other balances as I

think we may have a .................................................. error."

(e)   "Who was in charge of that trainee last week? He has entered the payment for the electricity

bill on the debit side of the bank and on the credit side of electricity – a ..............................

of .................................................."

(f)   "I found this purchase invoice from last week in amongst the copy letters. As we haven't put

it through the accounts we have an error of ......................................................."

**3.6** The following are the business transactions of Mark Tansall, a retailer of computer software, for the months of January and February 1999:

**Transactions for January**

1999

| | |
|---|---|
| 1 Jan | Started in business with capital of £10,000 in the bank |
| 4 Jan | Paid rent on premises £500, by cheque |
| 5 Jan | Bought shop fittings £5,000, by cheque |
| 7 Jan | Bought stock of software, £7,500, on credit from Tech Software |
| 11 Jan | Software sales £2,400, paid into bank |
| 12 Jan | Software sales £2,000, paid into bank |
| 16 Jan | Bought software £5,000, on credit from Datasoft Limited |
| 20 Jan | Software sales £1,500 to Wyvern School, a cheque being received |
| 22 Jan | Software sales £2,250, paid into bank |
| 25 Jan | Bought software from A & A Supplies £3,000, by cheque |
| 27 Jan | Wyvern School returned software £280, cheque refund sent |
| 29 Jan | Sold software on credit to Teme College, £2,495 |

**Transactions for February**

1999

| | |
|---|---|
| 2 Feb | Software sales £2,720, paid into bank |
| 4 Feb | Paid rent on premises £500, by cheque |
| 5 Feb | Bought shop fittings £1,550, by cheque |
| 10 Feb | Software sales £3,995, paid into bank |
| 12 Feb | Sent cheque, £7,500, to Tech Software |

15 Feb    Bought software £4,510, on credit from Tech Software

19 Feb    Sent cheque, £5,000, to Datasoft Limited

22 Feb    Software sales £1,930, paid into bank

23 Feb    Teme College returned software, £145

24 Feb    Software sales £2,145, paid into bank

25 Feb    Bought software £2,120, on credit from Associated Software

26 Feb    Software sales £4,150, paid into bank

**You are to:**

(a)    Record the January transactions in the books of account, and balance each account at 31 January 1999.

(b)    Draw up a trial balance at 31 January 1999.

(c)    Record the February transactions in the books of account, and balance each account at 28 February 1999.

(d)    Draw up a trial balance at 28 February 1999.

*Notes:*

- *Mark Tansall is not registered for Value Added Tax*
- *day books are not required*
- *make sure that you leave plenty of space for each account – particularly sales, purchases and bank*

Note: a pro-forma photocopiable extended trial balance is printed in the Appendix.

# 4 FINAL ACCOUNTS – THE EXTENDED TRIAL BALANCE

## Extended trial balance format

A photocopiable pro-forma of the extended trial balance is printed in the Appendix. If you wish to use this, it is advisable to enlarge it to A4 size. Alternatively you can set up a computer spreadsheet – but remember to allow for all the rows shown on the pro-forma – they will be needed in later chapters.

## Optional activities

The figures from the extended trial balance columns can, in addition, be extracted to set out statements of income and expenditure (to determine net profit) and totalled lists of assets, liabilities and capital. You may also wish to set out the final accounts in full as preparation for NVQ Level 4 work.

**4.1**  Which one of the following does not appear in the profit and loss account?

  (a)  closing stock

  (b)  purchases

  (c)  interest paid

  (d)  cash

  Answer (a) or (b) or (c) or (d)

**4.2**  Which one of the following does not appear in the balance sheet?

  (a)  closing stock

  (b)  sales

  (c)  debtors

  (d)  bank

  Answer (a) or (b) or (c) or (d)

**4.3**   The following trial balance has been extracted by the book-keeper of Matt Smith at 31  December 1998:

|  | Dr | Cr |
|---|---|---|
|  | £ | £ |
| Stock at 1 January 1998 | 14,350 |  |
| Purchases | 114,472 |  |
| Sales |  | 259,688 |
| Rates | 13,718 |  |
| Heating and lighting | 12,540 |  |
| Wages and salaries | 42,614 |  |
| Motor vehicle expenses | 5,817 |  |
| Advertising | 6,341 |  |
| Premises | 75,000 |  |
| Office equipment | 33,000 |  |
| Motor vehicles | 21,500 |  |
| Debtors | 23,854 |  |
| Bank | 1,235 |  |
| Cash | 125 |  |
| Capital |  | 62,500 |
| Drawings | 12,358 |  |
| Loan from bank |  | 35,000 |
| Creditors |  | 14,258 |
| Value Added Tax |  | 5,478 |
|  | 376,924 | 376,924 |

*Note:* stock at 31 December 1998 was valued at £16,280

**You are to** prepare the figures for the final accounts of Matt Smith for the year ended 31  December 1998, using the extended trial balance method.

**4.4** The following trial balance has been extracted by the book-keeper of Clare Lewis at 31 December 1998:

|  | Dr | Cr |
|---|---|---|
|  | £ | £ |
| Debtors | 18,600 | |
| Creditors | | 11,480 |
| Value Added Tax | | 1,870 |
| Bank overdraft | | 4,610 |
| Capital | | 25,250 |
| Sales | | 144,810 |
| Purchases | 96,318 | |
| Stock at 1 January 1998 | 16,010 | |
| Salaries | 18,465 | |
| Heating and lighting | 1,820 | |
| Rent and rates | 5,647 | |
| Motor vehicles | 9,820 | |
| Office equipment | 5,500 | |
| Sundry expenses | 845 | |
| Motor vehicle expenses | 1,684 | |
| Drawings | 13,311 | |
| | 188,020 | 188,020 |

*Note:* stock at 31 December 1998 was valued at £13,735

**You are to** prepare the figures for the final accounts of Clare Lewis for the year ended 31 December 1998, using the extended trial balance method.

**4.5** The trial balance of Jane Richardson, who runs a secretarial agency, has been prepared at 31 December 1999 as follows:

|  | Dr | Cr |
| --- | --- | --- |
|  | £ | £ |
| Capital |  | 25,000 |
| Office equipment | 30,000 |  |
| Income from clients |  | 75,450 |
| Administration | 3,280 |  |
| Wages | 37,145 |  |
| Rent paid | 8,052 |  |
| Telephone | 1,287 |  |
| Travel expenses | 926 |  |
| Rates | 2,355 |  |
| Debtors | 3,698 |  |
| Creditors |  | 1,074 |
| Value Added Tax |  | 2,021 |
| Bank | 3,971 |  |
| Cash | 241 |  |
| Drawings | 12,590 |  |
|  | 103,545 | 103,545 |

**You are to** prepare the figures for the final accounts of Jane Richardson for the year ended 31 December 1999, using the extended trial balance method.

Note: a pro-forma photocopiable extended
trial balance is printed in the Appendix.

# 5 ACCRUALS AND PREPAYMENTS

### Extended trial balance format

A photocopiable pro-forma of the extended trial balance is printed in the Appendix. If you wish to use this, it is advisable to enlarge it to A4 size. Alternatively you can set up a computer spreadsheet – but remember to allow for all the rows shown on the pro-forma – they will be needed in later chapters.

### Optional activities

The figures from the extended trial balance columns can, in addition, be extracted to set out statements of income and expenditure (to determine net profit) and totalled lists of assets, liabilities and capital. You may also wish to set out the final accounts in full as preparation for NVQ Level 4 work.

**5.1**    Show how the following will be recorded in the books of account:

(a)    Rent paid for the business premises is £500 per month. The rental for January 2000 was paid in December 1999 and is included in the total payments during 1999 which amounted to £6,500.

(b)    Motor vehicle expenses paid to 31 December 1999 amount to £8,455. On 4 January 2000 a fuel bill of £610 is received which relates to December. The bill is paid by cheque on 18 January 2000.

(c)    A claim has been made on the company's insurance policy for stock damaged in a small fire. On 16 December 1999, the amount of the claim has been agreed at £180. The amount is paid by the insurance company on 26 January 2000.

(d)    At 31 December 1999, the balance of telephone account is £500. Of this, £100 is the amount of personal calls made by the owner of the business.

**5.2**   Write short notes distinguishing between *income and expenditure accounting* and *receipts and payments accounting.*

**5.3**   A credit balance on accruals account indicates:

(a)   a liability and an expense owing

(b)   an asset and a prepayment of income

(c)   an asset and an accrual of income

(d)   a liability and an expense prepaid

Answer (a) or (b) or (c) or (d)

**5.4**   Which one of the following is a current asset?

(a)   creditors

(b)   accruals

(c)   machinery

(d)   prepayments

Answer (a) or (b) or (c) or (d)

**5.5** The following trial balance has been extracted by the book-keeper of Cindy Hayward, who runs a delicatessen shop, at 30 June 1999:

| | Dr £ | Cr £ |
|---|---|---|
| Capital | | 20,932 |
| Purchases | 148,500 | |
| Sales | | 210,900 |
| Repairs to buildings | 848 | |
| Delivery van | 5,000 | |
| Van expenses | 1,540 | |
| Land and buildings | 85,000 | |
| Loan from bank | | 50,000 |
| Bank | 540 | |
| Shop fittings | 2,560 | |
| Wages and salaries | 30,280 | |
| Discounts allowed | 135 | |
| Discounts received | | 1,319 |
| Rates and insurance | 2,690 | |
| Debtors | 3,175 | |
| Creditors | | 8,295 |
| Heating and lighting | 3,164 | |
| General expenses | 4,680 | |
| Sales returns | 855 | |
| Purchases returns | | 1,221 |
| Stock at 1 July 1998 | 6,210 | |
| Value Added Tax | | 2,510 |
| | 295,177 | 295,177 |

*Notes at 30 June 1999:*

- stock was valued at £7,515
- rates prepaid £255
- wages owing £560
- van expenses owing £85
- goods costing £200 were taken by Cindy Hayward for her own use

**You are to** prepare the figures for the final accounts of Cindy Hayward for the year ended 30 June 1999, using the extended trial balance method.

**5.6** The following list of balances has been extracted by the book-keeper of Southtown Supplies, a wholesaling business, at 31 December 1999:

|  | £ |
|---|---|
| Stock at 1 January 1999 | 70,000 |
| Purchases | 280,000 |
| Sales | 420,000 |
| Sales returns | 6,000 |
| Purchases returns | 4,500 |
| Discounts received | 750 |
| Discounts allowed | 500 |
| Electricity | 13,750 |
| Salaries | 35,600 |
| Post and packing | 1,400 |
| Premises | 120,000 |
| Fixtures and fittings | 45,000 |
| Debtors | 55,000 |
| Creditors | 47,000 |
| Bank balance | 5,000 |
| Capital | 195,000 |
| Drawings | 41,000 |
| Value Added Tax (amount due) | 6,000 |

*Notes at 31 December 1999:*

• stock was valued at £60,000; this figure excludes goods which were damaged by a burst water pipe and have been scrapped (no sale proceeds); Wyvern Insurance has agreed to cover the loss of £500 incurred in writing off the goods

• electricity owing £350

• salaries prepaid £400

**You are to** prepare the figures for the final accounts of Southtown Supplies for the year ended 31 December 1999, using the extended trial balance method.

Note: a pro-forma photocopiable extended trial balance is printed in the Appendix.

# 6 DEPRECIATION OF FIXED ASSETS

## Extended trial balance format

A photocopiable pro-forma of the extended trial balance is printed in the Appendix. If you wish to use this, it is advisable to enlarge it to A4 size. Alternatively you can set up a computer spreadsheet – but remember to allow for all the rows shown on the pro-forma – they will be needed in later chapters.

## Optional activities

The figures from the extended trial balance columns can, in addition, be extracted to set out statements of income and expenditure (to determine net profit) and totalled lists of assets, liabilities and capital. You may also wish to set out the final accounts in full as preparation for NVQ Level 4 work.

**6.1** A car which cost £20,000 is being depreciated at 30 per cent per year using the reducing balance method. At the end of three years it will have a net book value of:

(a) £2,000

(b) £6,860

(c) £13,140

(d) £18,000

Answer (a) or (b) or (c) or (d)

**6.2** The book-keeping entries to record a profit on sale of fixed assets are:

|  | Debit | Credit |
|---|---|---|
| (a) | fixed asset account | profit and loss account |
| (b) | disposals account | profit and loss account |
| (c) | profit and loss account | disposals account |
| (d) | bank account | profit and loss account |

Answer (a) or (b) or (c) or (d)

**6.3**  Martin Hough, sole owner of Juicyburger, a fast food shop, operating from leased premises in the town, is suspicious of his accountant, Mr S Harris, whom he claims doesn't really understand the food business. On the telephone he asks Mr Harris why depreciation is charged on a rigid formula, as surely no-one really knows how much his equipment is worth, and in fact he might not get anything for it. Draft a reply to Mr Hough from Mr Harris explaining the importance of depreciation and its application to final accounts.

**6.4**  Rachael Hall's financial year runs to 31 December. On 1 January 1999, her accounts show that she owns a car with an original cost of £12,000 and depreciation to date of £7,200.

On 1 October 1999, Rachael bought a new car at a cost of £15,000. She traded in the old car at a part-exchange value of £5,500 and paid the balance by cheque.

Rachael depreciates vehicles at 20 per cent per year using the straight-line method. Her accounting policy is to charge a full year's depreciation in the year of purchase, but none in the year of sale.

You are to show:

(a)     vehicles account for 1999

(b)     depreciation account for 1999

(c)     provision for depreciation account for 1999

(d)     asset disposal account for 1999

(e)     balance sheet extract at 31 December 1999

**6.5** The following trial balance has been extracted by the book-keeper of Wintergreen Supplies at 31 December 1999:

|  | Dr | Cr |
|---|---|---|
|  | £ | £ |
| Premises | 120,000 | |
| Long-term loan | | 60,000 |
| Capital | | 70,000 |
| Debtors | 1,900 | |
| Creditors | | 1,500 |
| Drawings | 6,750 | |
| Cash | 150 | |
| Stock at 1 January 1999 | 4,200 | |
| Fixtures and fittings at cost | 5,000 | |
| Provision for depreciation (fixtures and fittings) | | 1,000 |
| Vehicles at cost | 10,000 | |
| Provision for depreciation (vehicles) | | 2,000 |
| Bank | | 750 |
| Sales | | 195,000 |
| Purchases | 154,000 | |
| Wages | 20,500 | |
| Sundry expenses | 9,500 | |
| Value Added Tax | | 1,750 |
| | 332,000 | 332,000 |

*Notes at 31 December 1999:*

- stock was valued at £5,200
- vehicles and fixtures and fittings are to be depreciated at 20% (straight line)
- wages prepaid are £560, and sundry expenses accrued are £500
- premises are not to be depreciated

**You are to** prepare the figures for the final accounts of Wintergreen Supplies for the year ended 31 December 1999, using the extended trial balance method.

**6.6**  Cindy Smith owns an engineering supplies business, and the following trial balance has been extracted by her book-keeper at 30 June 1999:

|  | Dr | Cr |
|---|---|---|
|  | £ | £ |
| Capital |  | 38,825 |
| Stock at 1 July 1998 | 18,050 |  |
| Purchases | 74,280 |  |
| Sales |  | 149,410 |
| Discounts | 3,210 | 1,140 |
| Rent and rates | 7,280 |  |
| Returns | 1,645 | 875 |
| Cash | 820 |  |
| Bank |  | 13,300 |
| Debtors and creditors | 14,375 | 8,065 |
| Wages and salaries | 43,895 |  |
| General expenses | 2,515 |  |
| Motor vehicles at cost | 30,000 |  |
| Provision for depreciation on motor vehicles |  | 7,500 |
| Fixtures and fittings at cost | 10,000 |  |
| Provision for depreciation on fixtures and fittings |  | 3,000 |
| Motor vehicle expenses | 6,725 |  |
| Drawings | 12,500 |  |
| Value Added Tax |  | 3,180 |
|  | 225,295 | 225,295 |

*Notes at 30 June 1999:*

•  stock was valued at £20,145

•  general expenses owing £175

•  rates prepaid £95

•  depreciate motor vehicles at 25 per cent per annum, using the reducing balance method

•  depreciate fixtures and fittings at 10 per cent per annum, using the straight line method

**You are to** prepare the figures for the final accounts of Cindy Smith for the year ended 30 June 1999, using the extended trial balance method.

Note: a pro-forma photocopiable extended trial balance is printed in the Appendix.

# 7 BAD DEBTS AND PROVISION FOR BAD DEBTS

## Extended trial balance format

A photocopiable pro-forma of the extended trial balance is printed in the Appendix. If you wish to use this, it is advisable to enlarge it to A4 size. Alternatively you can set up a computer spreadsheet – but remember to allow for all the rows shown on the pro-forma – they will be needed in later chapters.

## Optional activities

The figures from the extended trial balance columns can, in addition, be extracted to set out statements of income and expenditure (to determine net profit) and totalled lists of assets, liabilities and capital. You may also wish to set out the final accounts in full as preparation for NVQ Level 4 work.

**7.1** The accounts supervisor at the firm where you work has instructed you to write off a debtor's account as bad. Which one of the following double-entry book-keeping entries will you make?

|     | *Debit*                      | *Credit*                      |
|-----|------------------------------|-------------------------------|
| (a) | debtor's account             | bad debts written off account |
| (b) | bank account                 | debtor's account              |
| (c) | bad debts written off account| debtor's account              |
| (d) | debtor's account             | provision for bad debts account |

Answer (a) or (b) or (c) or (d)

*Ignore VAT relief on bad debt write-off.*

**7.2** An increase in provision for bad debts will:

(a) decrease net profit for the year

(b) be recorded in the debtors' accounts

(c) decrease the cash/bank balance

(d) increase net profit for the year

Answer (a) or (b) or (c) or (d)

**7.3** The profit and loss account of a business has been prepared showing a net loss of £2,350. A reduction of £150 in the provision of bad debts should have been made, and bad debts of £70 should have been written off. Net loss will now be:

(a) £2,130

(b) £2,270

(c) £2,430

(d) £2,570

Answer (a) or (b) or (c) or (d)

*Ignore VAT relief on bad debt write-off.*

**7.4** You are the book-keeper at Enterprise Trading Company. The following information is available for the financial years ending 31 December 1998, 1999, 2000:

        £

- Debtor balances at 31 December 1998, before writing off bad debts   105,200

- Bad debts written off on 31 December 1998   1,800

- 2.5% provision for bad debts created at 31 December 1998

- Debtor balances at 31 December 1999, before writing off bad debts   115,600

- Bad debts written off on 31 December 1999   2,400

- 2.5% provision for bad debts adjusted in line with the change in the level of debtors at 31 December 1999

- Debtor balances at 31 December 2000, before writing off bad debts   110,200

- Bad debts written off on 31 December 2000   1,400

- 2.5% provision for bad debts adjusted in line with the change in the level of debtors at 31 December 2000

*Note: ignore VAT relief on bad debt write-off*

**You are to**:

(a) write up the following accounts for 1998, 1999 and 2000 (see pages 28 and 29):

   – bad debts written off

   – provision for bad debts: adjustment

   – provision for bad debts

(b) show the effect of these transactions in the following table:

| YEAR | PROFIT AND LOSS ACCOUNT | | | | BALANCE SHEET | | |
|---|---|---|---|---|---|---|---|
| | Expense | | Income | | | | |
| | Bad debts | Prov for bad debts | Bad debts | Prov for bad debts | Debtors | Less prov for bad debts | Net debtors |
| | £ | £ | £ | £ | £ | £ | £ |
| 1998 | | | | | | | |
| 1999 | | | | | | | |
| 2000 | | | | | | | |

Dr                    **BAD DEBTS WRITTEN OFF ACCOUNT**                    Cr

| Date | Details | Amount | Date | Details | Amount |
|------|---------|--------|------|---------|--------|
|      |         | £      |      |         | £      |
|      |         |        |      |         |        |
|      |         |        |      |         |        |
|      |         |        |      |         |        |
|      |         |        |      |         |        |
|      |         |        |      |         |        |
|      |         |        |      |         |        |

Dr         **PROVISION FOR BAD DEBTS: ADJUSTMENT ACCOUNT**         Cr

| Date | Details | Amount | Date | Details | Amount |
|------|---------|--------|------|---------|--------|
|      |         | £      |      |         | £      |
|      |         |        |      |         |        |
|      |         |        |      |         |        |
|      |         |        |      |         |        |
|      |         |        |      |         |        |
|      |         |        |      |         |        |
|      |         |        |      |         |        |

**Dr**        **PROVISION FOR BAD DEBTS ACCOUNT**        Cr

| Date | Details | Amount | Date | Details | Amount |
|------|---------|--------|------|---------|--------|
|      |         | £      |      |         | £      |
|      |         |        |      |         |        |

**7.5** The accounts supervisor at the firm where you work hands you a cheque for £50 received from a former debtor, James Abel, whose account was written off as bad last year. The cheque is in part settlement of the amount owed by James Abel.

You are to record the transaction in the firm's double-entry accounts. Use today's date in the accounts and ignore any VAT implications in the transaction.

Rule up your own accounts, or photocopy the blank ledger accounts in the Appendix.

*Note: the accounts shown on these two pages are intended for use in Activity 7.4.*

**7.6** The following trial balance has been extracted by the book-keeper of Jane Jones, who sells carpets, as at 31 December 1999:

|  | Dr £ | Cr £ |
|---|---|---|
| Debtors | 37,200 | |
| Creditors | | 30,640 |
| Value Added Tax | | 4,280 |
| Bank | 14,640 | |
| Capital | | 50,500 |
| Sales | | 289,620 |
| Purchases | 182,636 | |
| Stock at 1 January 1999 | 32,020 | |
| Wages and salaries | 36,930 | |
| Heat and light | 3,640 | |
| Rent and rates | 11,294 | |
| Vehicles | 20,000 | |
| Provision for depreciation on vehicles | | 4,000 |
| Equipment | 10,000 | |
| Provision for depreciation on equipment | | 1,000 |
| Sundry expenses | 1,690 | |
| Motor expenses | 3,368 | |
| Drawings | 26,622 | |
| | 380,040 | 380,040 |

*Notes at 31 December 1999:*

- stock was valued at £34,000
- bad debts of £2,200 are to be written off and a provision for bad debts of 5% is to be created
- vehicles are to be depreciated at 20% per annum and equipment at 10% per annum (both using the reducing balance method)
- there are sundry expenses accruals of £270, and rates prepayments of £2,190

**You are to** prepare the figures for the final accounts of Jane Jones for the year ended 31 December 1999, using the extended trial balance method.

**7.7**   The following trial balance has been extracted by the book-keeper of Andrew Brown, a fashion designer, as at 31 December 1999:

|  | Dr | Cr |
|---|---|---|
|  | £ | £ |
| Purchases | 31,480 |  |
| Sales |  | 95,660 |
| Stock at 1 January 1999 | 7,580 |  |
| Returns | 240 | 620 |
| Discounts | 380 | 1,080 |
| Drawings | 34,720 |  |
| Premises | 100,000 |  |
| Fixtures and fittings | 24,000 |  |
| Provision for depreciation on fixtures and fittings |  | 3,000 |
| Wages and salaries | 18,620 |  |
| Advertising | 2,260 |  |
| Rates | 8,240 |  |
| Sundry expenses | 7,390 |  |
| Bank | 4,020 |  |
| Cash | 120 |  |
| Debtors | 5,000 |  |
| Bad debts written off | 100 |  |
| Provision for bad debts |  | 520 |
| Creditors |  | 3,740 |
| Value Added Tax |  | 3,240 |
| Capital |  | 81,290 |
| Bank loan |  | 55,000 |
|  | 244,150 | 244,150 |

*Notes at 31 December 1999:*
- stock was valued at £6,060
- depreciation is to be provided on fixtures and fittings at 12.5% per annum using the straight line method
- provision for bad debts is to be 5% of debtors
- wages accrued are £500, and advertising prepaid is £350
- premises are not to be depreciated

**You are to** prepare the figures for the final accounts of Andrew Brown for the year ended 31 December 1999, using the extended trial balance method.

# 8 THE REGULATORY FRAMEWORK OF ACCOUNTING

**8.1** (a) Explain the accounting concept of materiality.

(b) Suggest three types of situation to which the concept of materiality is applicable.

(c) Suggest two problems which may occur when applying the concept of materiality.

**8.2** Eveshore Electronics Limited imports electronic goods from the Far East and sells to retailers in the UK. The company has always valued its stock on the FIFO (first in, first out) basis. One of the directors comments that, because of the recent strength of the pound sterling against Far Eastern currencies, the price of imported electronic goods has been falling throughout the year. She suggests that the closing stock should be recalculated on the LIFO (last in, first out) basis.

(a) Assuming that the prices of electronic goods have been falling throughout the year, would the change suggested increase profit for the year, decrease profit, or would profit remain the same?

(b) Which accounting concept states that a business should not normally change its basis for valuing stock unless it has good reasons for so doing?

**8.3** A business buys twenty units of a product in January at a cost of £3.00 each; it buys ten more in February at £3.50 each, and ten in April at £4.00 each. Eight units are sold in March, and sixteen are sold in May.

**You are to** calculate the value of closing stock at the end of May using:

(a) FIFO (first in, first out)

(b) LIFO (last in, first out)

(c) AVCO (average cost)

*Note: where appropriate, work to the nearest penny.*

**8.4**    Wyvern Office Supplies sells a range of pens, paper, computer supplies and other office sundries. One of its lines is photocopying paper for which the stock movements in January 1999 were:

| | |
|---|---|
| 1 January | Stock of 800 reams (a ream is 500 sheets) of photocopying paper brought forward at a cost of £2.00 per ream |
| 5 January | Sold 700 reams |
| 11 January | Bought 1,200 reams at £2.20 per ream |
| 15 January | Sold 600 reams |
| 19 January | Bought 1,000 reams at £2.10 per ream |
| 21 January | Sold 400 reams |
| 26 January | Bought 700 reams at £2.25 per ream |

The selling price of each ream is £3.25.

**You are to** calculate the value of:

(a)    sales for January

(b)    the closing stock at 31 January and cost of sales for January, assuming that stock is valued on the FIFO (first in, first out) basis

(c)    the closing stock at 31 January and cost of sales for January, assuming that stock is valued on the LIFO (last in, first out) basis

**8.5**    YZ Limited is formed on 1 January 1999 and trades in two products, Y and Z. At the end of its first half-year the stock movements of the two products are as follows:

| 1999 | PRODUCT Y | | PRODUCT Z | |
|---|---|---|---|---|
| | Bought (units) | Sold (units) | Bought (units) | Sold (units) |
| January | 100 at £4.00 | | 200 at £10.00 | |
| February | | 80 at £10.00 | 100 at   £9.50 | |
| March | 140 at £4.20 | | | 240 at £16.00 |
| April | 100 at £3.80 | | 100 at £10.50 | |
| May | | 140 at £10.00 | 140 at £10.00 | |
| June | 80 at £4.50 | | | 100 at £16.00 |

The company values stock on the FIFO (first in, first out) basis.

At 30 June 1999, the net realisable value of each type of stock is:

|  |  |
|---|---|
| product Y | £1,750.00 |
| product Z | £1,950.00 |
| | £3,700.00 |

**You are to** calculate the value of:

(a)    total sales for the half-year

(b)    the closing stock at 30 June 1999 for each product using the FIFO basis

(c)    the total at which the company's stocks should be valued on 30 June 1999 in order to comply with standard accounting practice

(d)    cost of sales for the half-year in order to comply with standard accounting practice

**8.6**    Which one of the following is revenue expenditure?

(a)    purchase of a computer for the office

(b)    legal costs for the purchase of property

(c)    cost of extension to property

(d)    quarterly electricity bill

Answer (a) or (b) or (c) or (d)

**8.7**  Which one of the following is capital expenditure?

(a)  repairs to motor vehicles

(b)  goods taken by owner for own use

(c)  cost of raw materials used in extending the premises

(d)  renewing the electrical wiring in the office

Answer (a) or (b) or (c) or (d)

**8.8**  Wages paid to own employees who have redecorated the office are:

(a)  capital expenditure

(b)  debited to profit and loss account

(d)  debited to premises account

(d)  credited to profit and loss account

Answer (a) or (b) or (c) or (d)

**8.9**  Classify the following costs (tick the appropriate column):

| | capital expenditure | revenue expenditure |
|---|---|---|
| (a)  purchase of motor vehicles | | |
| (b)  depreciation of motor vehicles | | |
| (c)  rent paid on premises | | |
| (d)  wages and salaries | | |
| (e)  legal fees relating to the purchase of property | | |
| (f)  re-decoration of office | | |
| (g)  installation of air-conditioning in office | | |
| (h)  wages of own employees used to build extension to the stockroom | | |
| (i)  installation and setting up of a new machine | | |

Note: a set of photocopiable blank ledger accounts is printed in the Appendix.

# 9 CONTROL ACCOUNTS

**9.1** Would the following errors cause a difference between the balance of the sales ledger control account and the total of the balances in the sales ledger?

(a) The sales returns day book was undercast by £100.

(b) The amount of a credit note issued was credited to the account of Martley Traders instead of Martley Manufacturing.

**9.2** On 31 December 1998 the balances of the memorandum accounts in the purchases ledger of Thomas Limited were listed, totalled, and compared with the balance of the purchases ledger control account. The total of the list of balances amounted to £55,946. Investigations were carried out and the following errors were discovered:

(a) a creditor balance of £553 had been listed as £535

(b) cash discount received of £100 had been credited to the creditor's account

(c) a credit note received for £141 (including VAT) had not been recorded in the creditor's account

(d) a creditor balance of £225 had been listed twice

**You are to** record the appropriate adjustments in the table below; show clearly the amount involved and whether it is to be added or subtracted.

|  | | £ |
|---|---|---|
| Total of list of creditor balances | | 55,946 |
| Adjustment for (a) | add/subtract | ................ |
| Adjustment for (b) | add/subtract | ................ |
| Adjustment for (c) | add/subtract | ................ |
| Adjustment for (d) | add/subtract | ................ |
| Revised total to agree with purchases ledger control account | | |

**9.3** The following accounts, together with their balances at 1 January 1999, form the purchases ledger of A Austin:

| | |
|---|---|
| B Bedford | £596.41 |
| C Chrysler | £602.03 |
| D De Lorean | £228.14 |
| F Ford | £487.29 |

During January the following transactions took place:

5 Jan   Bought goods on credit from C Chrysler £127.55 and from F Ford £298.31

7 Jan   Bought goods on credit from B Bedford £348.19 and from D De Lorean £422.19

11 Jan   Returned goods to C Chrysler £12.34 and to B Bedford £59.68

15 Jan   Paid D De Lorean £250.00 on account, by cheque

21 Jan   Paid F Ford by cheque the balance owing on the account after deducting a 5% cash discount

**You are to:**

(a)   write up the personal accounts in the purchases ledger of A Austin for January 1999, balancing them at the end of the month

(b)   prepare a purchases ledger control account for January 1999, balancing it at the end of the month

(c)   reconcile the control account balance with the creditors' accounts at 31 January 1999

*Note: VAT is to be ignored on all transactions and day books are not required.*

**9.4**    The purchases ledger of Rowcester Traders contains the following accounts on 1 February 1998:

Arley Supplies Limited, balance £1,549.81 credit

Balfour Brothers, balance £39.20 debit

W James & Company, balance £598.27 credit

Mereford Manufacturing Company, balance £495.83 credit

Northern Equipment Limited, balance £727.86 credit

W Williams, balance £1,040.40 credit

The following transactions took place during February:

3 Feb    Bought goods on credit from Arley Supplies Limited, £986.28, and from Balfour Brothers £1,167.24

6 Feb    Paid W Williams a cheque for the balance of the account after deducting 2.5% cash discount

10 Feb    Bought goods on credit from W James & Company £452.13, and from W Williams £1,595.26

11 Feb    Paid Northern Equipment Limited a cheque for the balance of the account

16 Feb    Returned goods to Arley Supplies Limited for £236.09

17 Feb    Paid Arley Supplies a cheque for the balance of the account, after deducting 2.5% cash discount

18 Feb    Returned goods to Northern Equipment Limited for £97.39

24 Feb    Paid W James & Company the amount owing by cheque, after deducting 2.5% cash discount

26 Feb    Bought goods on credit from Arley Supplies Limited £699.84

28 Feb    Transfer of debit balance of £364.68 in the sales ledger to Mereford Manufacturing Company's account in the purchases ledger

**You are to:**

(a)    write up the personal accounts in the purchases ledger of Rowcester Traders for February 1998, balancing them at the end of the month

(b)    prepare a purchases ledger control account for February 1998, balancing it at the end of the month

(c)    reconcile the control account balance with the creditors' accounts at 1 February and 28 February 1998

*Note: VAT is to be ignored on all transactions and day books are not required.*

**9.5**   Prepare purchases ledger control and sales ledger control accounts for the year-ended 31 December 1998 from the following information:

### BALANCES AT 1 JANUARY 1998

*   debtors, £35,650 debit, £87 credit

*   creditors, £24,080 credit

### TOTALS FOR THE YEAR FROM THE DAY BOOKS

*   sales day book, £205,610

*   purchases day book, £137,825

*   sales returns day book, £3,081

*   purchases returns day book, £1,843

### TOTALS FOR THE YEAR FROM THE CASH BOOK

*   discount allowed, £548

*   payments received from debtors, £197,045

*   discount received, £494

*   payments made to creditors, £135,048

*   debtors' cheques returned unpaid, £856

### OTHER TRANSACTIONS

*   set-off entries between sales ledger and purchases ledger, £812

*   bad debts written off, £110

*   increase in provision for bad debts, £250

At 31 December 1998 there were no debtors' accounts with credit balances; there was one creditor's account with a debit balance of £112.

**9.6**  Carpminster Limited uses control accounts for its purchases ledger and sales ledger. At 1 September 1998 the balances of the control accounts were:

| | Debit | Credit |
|---|---|---|
| | £ | £ |
| Purchases ledger | 495 | 78,039 |
| Sales ledger | 103,831 | 682 |

The following transactions took place during September 1998:

| | £ |
|---|---|
| Credit purchases | 154,648 |
| Credit sales | 210,076 |
| Sales returns | 3,089 |
| Purchases returns | 7,307 |
| Cash/cheques received from debtors | 198,364 |
| Cash/cheques paid to creditors | 136,834 |
| Customers' cheques dishonoured | 210 |
| Cash discount allowed | 3,117 |
| Cash discount received | 1,541 |
| Bad debts written off | 384 |
| Transfer of a credit balance from the purchases ledger to the sales ledger | 1,097 |

At 30 September 1998, there were debit balances in the purchases ledger of £362 and credit balances in the sales ledger of £246.

**You are to:**

• prepare the purchases ledger control account and sales ledger control account at Carpminster Limited for September 1998

• balance the accounts at 30 September 1998

Note: a photocopiable blank journal page is printed in the Appendix.

# 10 THE JOURNAL – CORRECTION OF ERRORS

*For journal entries involving sales ledger and purchases ledger, it is to be assumed that control accounts are incorporated into the double-entry book-keeping system and that the accounts for each debtor and creditor are kept in memorandum form.*

**10.1** Which one of the following will not be recorded in the journal?

(a)    opening transaction of a new business

(b)    goods taken by the owner for her own use

(c)    closing stock valuation at the year end

(d)    petty cash payment for office window cleaning

Answer (a) or (b) or (c) or (d)

**10.2** The purchase of stationery, £25, has been debited in error to office equipment account. Which one of the following journal entries will correct the error?

|     | *Debit*          |      | *Credit*         |      |
| --- | ---------------- | ---- | ---------------- | ---- |
| (a) | Office equipment | £25  | Stationery       | £25  |
| (b) | Suspense         | £25  | Office equipment | £25  |
| (c) | Stationery       | £25  | Office equipment | £25  |
| (d) | Stationery       | £25  | Suspense         | £25  |

*Note: VAT is to be ignored*

Answer (a) or (b) or (c) or (d)

**10.3** A trial balance fails to agree by £27 and the difference is placed to a suspense account. Later it is found that a payment for postages of £63 has been entered in the accounts as £36. Which one of the following journal entries will correct the error?

|     | *Debit*              |            | *Credit*             |            |
| --- | -------------------- | ---------- | -------------------- | ---------- |
| (a) | Suspense<br>Postages | £36<br>£63 | Postages<br>Suspense | £36<br>£63 |
| (b) | Suspense             | £27        | Postages             | £27        |
| (c) | Postages             | £27        | Bank                 | £27        |
| (d) | Postages<br>Suspense | £36<br>£63 | Suspense<br>Postages | £36<br>£63 |

Answer (a) or (b) or (c) or (d)

**10.4**  What is the effect on the previously-calculated profit and the balance sheet of each of the following?

(a)      sales account has been overcast by £1,000

(b)      closing stock has been undervalued by £250

(c)      telephone expenses account has been undercast by £100

(d)      discount received of £135 has been omitted

(e)      depreciation of the vehicles of £1,250 for the year has not been made

(f)      a reduction of £100 in provision for bad debts has not been made

(g)      bad debts totalling £75 have not been written off

**10.5**  You have recently taken over writing up the double-entry accounts of Manston Sales Limited. You have found a number of errors made by the previous book-keeper as follows:

(a)      credit sale of goods for £250 to Didsbury Limited has not been entered in the accounts

(b)      a cheque for £195 paid to William Thomas, a creditor, has been debited to the account of another creditor, Thomas Williams

(c)      office stationery costing £50 has been debited to office equipment account

(d)      a credit purchase of goods for £167 from A Carver has been entered in the accounts as £176

(e)      the total of purchases returns day book has been undercast by £100 as has electricity account

**You are to** take each error in turn and:

•      state the type of error

•      show the correcting journal entry

*Note: VAT is to be ignored.*

**10.6** Dave James is the book-keeper for Western Traders Limited. At 30 June 1999 he is unable to balance the trial balance. The difference, £86 credit, is placed to a suspense account in the general ledger pending further investigation.

The following errors are later found:

(a) sales account is overcast by £100

(b) a payment cheque for postages, £65, has been recorded in postages account as £56

(c) commission received of £150 has been debited to both the commission received account and the bank account

(d) stationery expenses of £105, paid by cheque, have not been entered in the expenses account

**You are to:**

• make journal entries to correct the errors

• show the suspense account after the errors have been corrected

*Note: VAT is to be ignored*

**10.7** Show the journal entries for the following transfers which relate to Jim Hoddle's business for the year ended 30 June 1999:

(a) closing stock is to be recorded in the accounts at a valuation of £15,500

(b) postages account has a balance of £1,800, but the franking machine meter shows that there is £200 unused; the amount due for the year is to be transferred to profit and loss account

(c) salaries and wages account has a balance of £45,500, but £1,500 is owing; the amount due for the year is to be transferred to profit and loss account

(d) depreciation on vehicles for the year is calculated at £3,000

(e) bad debts written off account has a balance of £180; the amount is to be transferred to profit and loss account

(f) the provision for bad debts is £250; the amount is to be increased to £300

# 11 BANK RECONCILIATION STATEMENTS

**11.1** A firm's bank statement shows an overdraft of £600. Unpresented cheques total £250; outstanding lodgements total £1,000. What is the balance shown by the firm's cash book?

(a)     £150

(b)     £650

(c)     £250 overdraft

(d)     £150 overdraft

Answer (a) or (b) or (c) or (d)


**11.2** Upon receipt of a bank statement, which one of the following must be written into the firm's cash book?

(a)     cheque debited in error by the bank

(b)     unpresented cheques

(c)     BACS receipts

(d)     outstanding lodgements

Answer (a) or (b) or (c) or (d)


**11.3** Heath Traders Limited requires the bank statement and cash book balances (bank columns) to be reconciled. You are given the following information as at 30 June 1999:

- the bank columns of the cash book show an overdraft of £1,250 at the bank

- cheques for £140, £110 and £60 have been sent out in payment to various suppliers but have not yet been paid into the bank by those suppliers; they are recorded in the cash book

- a direct debit payment of £40 has been recorded by the bank, but has not yet been entered in the cash book

- a cheque for £600 has been recorded as a receipt in the cash book, and paid into the bank; it has not yet been credited by the bank

- bank charges amounting to £25 appear on the bank statement, but have not yet been entered in the cash book

- a bank giro credit from a customer for £250 appears on the bank statement, but has not yet been entered in the cash book

- the bank statement shows a closing bank overdraft of £1,355

**You are to:**

(a)     write the cash book up-to-date at 30 June 1999

(b)     prepare a bank reconciliation statement at 30 June 1999

**11.4** The bank columns of David Smith's cash book for March 1999 are as follows:

| 1999 | Receipts | £ | 1999 | Payments | | £ |
|---|---|---|---|---|---|---|
| 1 Mar | Balance b/d | 755.50 | 4 Mar | Curtis Ltd | 001531 | 200.00 |
| 8 Mar | Johnson Limited | 530.90 | 12 Mar | T Daniels | 001532 | 327.40 |
| 29 Mar | Reid & Co | 386.45 | 15 Mar | Smith & Co | 001533 | 289.60 |
| | | | 16 Mar | Arnold & Sons | 001534 | 327.20 |
| | | | 22 Mar | P Singh | 001535 | 154.30 |
| | | | 31 Mar | Balance c/d | | 374.35 |
| | | 1,672.85 | | | | 1,672.85 |

He received his bank statement which showed the following transactions for March 1999:

| BANK STATEMENT | | Payments | Receipts | Balance |
|---|---|---|---|---|
| 1999 | | £ | £ | £ |
| 1 Mar | Balance brought forward | | | 736.45 CR |
| 4 Mar | Credit | | 274.30 | 1,010.75 CR |
| 8 Mar | Cheque no 001531 | 200.00 | | 810.75 CR |
| 8 Mar | Credit | | 530.90 | 1,341.65 CR |
| 10 Mar | Cheque no 001530 | 255.25 | | 1,086.40 CR |
| 15 Mar | BACS credit: A J Trading | | 396.20 | 1,482.60 CR |
| 22 Mar | Cheque no 001532 | 327.40 | | 1,155.20 CR |
| 24 Mar | Direct debit: Arley Finance | 184.65 | | 970.55 CR |
| 25 Mar | Cheque no 001533 | 289.60 | | 680.95 CR |

**You are to:**

(a)    write the cash book up-to-date at 31 March 1999

(b)    prepare an opening bank reconciliation statement at 1 March 1999

(c)    prepare a bank reconciliation statement at 31 March 1999

**11.5** You are the trainee cashier at Wyvern Trading Limited, working under the supervision of the office manager. The bank columns of the company's cash book for the week commencing 7 June 1999 are as follows:

| 1999 | Receipts | £ | 1999 | Payments | | £ |
|------|----------|---|------|----------|---|---|
| 7 Jun | Balance b/d | 986.40 | 7 Jun | Mega Books Ltd | 654321 | 406.29 |
| 7 Jun | Wyvern Council | 428.15 | 7 Jun | Cash | 654322 | 250.00 |
| 10 Jun | Abacus & Co | 752.00 | 8 Jun | Western Telecom | 654323 | 186.45 |
| 10 Jun | ITI Plc | 552.16 | 10 Jun | Wages | 654324 | 522.15 |
| | | | 11 Jun | College Supplies Ltd | 654325 | 342.87 |

The bank statement was received which showed the following transactions for the week:

| BANK STATEMENT | | Payments | Receipts | Balance |
|----------------|--|----------|----------|---------|
| 1999 | | £ | £ | £ |
| 7 Jun | Balance brought forward | | | 1,199.20 CR |
| 7 Jun | Credit | | 428.15 | 1,627.35 CR |
| 7 Jun | Cheque no 654322 | 250.00 | | 1,377.35 CR |
| 9 Jun | Cheque no 654320 | 212.80 | | 1,164.55 CR |
| 10 Jun | Direct debit: Westmid Finance Co | 107.25 | | 1,057.30 CR |
| 10 Jun | Cheque no 654324 | 522.15 | | 535.15 CR |
| 10 Jun | Credit | | 752.00 | 1,287.15 CR |
| 10 Jun | Bank giro credit: Johnson Plc | | 398.52 | 1,685.67 CR |
| 11 Jun | Cheque no 654321 | 406.29 | | 1,279.38 CR |
| 11 Jun | Cheque no 888901 | 50.00 | | 1,229.38 CR |
| 11 Jun | Bank charges | 17.50 | | 1,211.88 CR |

**You are to:**

(a) write the cash book up-to-date for the week commencing 7 June 1999

(b) prepare an opening bank reconciliation statement at 7 June 1999

(c) prepare a bank reconciliation statement at 11 June 1999

(d) write a memorandum to the office manager regarding any matter that you think should be queried with the bank

# 12 INCOMPLETE RECORDS

**12.1** James Hendry owns a business which sells office stationery. Most of his customers are firms in the area, to whom he sells on credit terms. Although he does not keep a full set of accounting records, the following information is available in respect of the year ended 31 December 1999:

**Summary of assets and liabilities:**

|  | 1 Jan 1999 | 31 Dec 1999 |
|---|---|---|
|  | £ | £ |
| Shop fittings (cost £10,000) | 8,000 | 7,000 |
| Stock | 25,600 | 29,800 |
| Bank balance | 4,000 | 8,000 |
| Cash | 1,000 | 1,600 |
| Debtors | 29,200 | 20,400 |
| Creditors | 20,800 | 16,000 |
| Accrual: business expenses | – | 500 |

**Summary of the business bank account for the year ended 31 December 1999:**

|  | £ |
|---|---|
| Receipts from customers | 127,800 |
| Payments to suppliers | 82,600 |
| Drawings | 20,000 |
| Business expenses | 20,600 |

**Other information**

Shop fittings are being depreciated at 10% per year, using the straight line method.

**You are to:**

(a) calculate the amount of sales during the year

(b) calculate the amount of purchases during the year

(c) calculate the figure for business expenses to be shown in the profit and loss account for the year ended 31 December 1999

(d) prepare James Hendry's profit and loss account for the year ended 31 December 1999

(e) prepare a list of assets, liabilities and capital as at 31 December 1999

(f) optional task: draw up James Hendry's balance sheet as at 31 December 1999

*Note: VAT is to be ignored on all transactions*

**12.2**   Colin Smith owns a business which sells specialist central heating parts to trade customers. He has been in business for a number of years. Although he does not keep a full set of accounting records, the following information is available in respect of the year ended 30 June 1999:

**Summary of assets and liabilities:**

|  | 1 July 1998 | 30 June 1999 |
|---|---|---|
|  | £ | £ |
| **Assets** |  |  |
| Stock | 25,000 | 27,500 |
| Fixtures and fittings (cost £50,000) | 40,000 | 35,000 |
| Debtors | 36,000 | 35,000 |
| Bank | 1,500 | 1,210 |
|  |  |  |
| **Liabilities** |  |  |
| Creditors | 32,500 | 30,000 |
| Accrual: business expenses | 500 | 700 |

**Summary of the business bank account for the year ended 30 June 1999:**

|  | £ |
|---|---|
| Business expenses | 30,000 |
| Drawings | 28,790 |
| Receipts from debtors | 121,000 |
| Payments to suppliers | 62,500 |

**Other information:**

- Fixtures and fittings are being depreciated at 10% per year using the straight line method
- Bad debts of £550 have been written off during the year

**You are to:**

(a)   Calculate the amount of sales during the year ended 30 June 1999

(b)   Calculate the amount of purchases during the year ended 30 June 1999

(c)   Calculate the figure for business expenses to be shown in the profit and loss account for the year ended 30 June 1999

(d)   Prepare Colin Smith's profit and loss account for the year ended 30 June 1999

(e)   Prepare a list of assets, liabilities and capital as at 30 June 1999

(f)   *optional task:* draw up Colin Smith's balance sheet as at 30 June 1999

*Note: VAT is to be ignored on all transactions*

**12.3**   You are preparing the 1998 accounts of Heidi Johnson, who runs a mobile carpet and curtain cleaning business. Heidi keeps few accounting records, but the person who prepared the accounts last year has left a set of working accounts with start of year balances. The balances have been entered in the accounts.

From Heidi's business bank statements you have prepared the following summary for the year ended 31 December 1998:

|  | £ | £ |
|---|---|---|
| Opening balance | | 1,547 |
| Receipts: | | |
| Cash takings | 2,150 | |
| Receipts from debtors | 55,290 | |
| Inheritance | 12,000 | 69,440 |
| | | 70,987 |
| Payments: | | |
| Payments to creditors | 18,450 | |
| Drawings | 20,000 | |
| Vehicle expenses | 4,250 | |
| General expenses | 4,100 | |
| Assistant's wages | 9,200 | |
| Purchase of new van on 1 July 1998 | 13,500 | 69,500 |
| Closing balance | | 1,487 |

The following information is available:

- At 31 December 1998, vehicle expenses were prepaid by £210.
- At 31 December 1998, assistant's wages of £480 were owing.
- At 31 December 1998, debtors were £6,410; creditors were £2,890.
- Invoices to customers during the year totalled £61,450.
- Heidi thinks that debtors amounting to £460 will not pay, and should be written off as bad debts.
- Some customers pay by cheque, while others pay in cash. Heidi has kept no records of the cash received but knows that she paid general expenses of £220 in cash; the rest she kept as drawings. At 31 December 1998, she had a cash float of £125.
- The inheritance was received from the estate of her grandmother: the amount was paid into the business bank account to help finance the new van. (She will keep her old van in order to provide flexibility when she and her assistant are working on different sites.)
- Heidi depreciates vans, using the straight line method, on the basis of a five-year life from the date of acquisition, with a nil residual value.
- At 31 December 1998 there was a stock of cleaning materials valued at £1,430.

**You are to** reconstruct the ledger accounts for the year ended 31 December 1998, showing the balances carried forward at the end of the year and/or the amounts to be transferred to profit and loss account. Ledger accounts with appropriate balances are set out on pages 50 to 55.

*Notes:*

- dates are not required
- the following accounts are not supplied and do not need to be shown:
  - profit and loss
  - sales
  - purchases
  - capital
- VAT is to be ignored on all transactions

| Dr | | **Bank Account** | | Cr |
|---|---|---|---|---|
| Details | Amount | Details | | Amount |
| | £ | | | £ |
| Balance b/d | 1,547 | | | |
| | | | | |
| | | | | |
| | | | | |

| Dr | | **Cash Account** | | Cr |
|---|---|---|---|---|
| Details | Amount | Details | | Amount |
| | £ | | | £ |
| Balance b/d | 86 | | | |
| | | | | |
| | | | | |
| | | | | |

Dr                 **Vehicle Expenses Account**                 Cr

| Details | Amount | Details | Amount |
|---------|--------|---------|--------|
|         | £      |         | £      |
|         |        | Balance b/d | 105 |
|         |        |         |        |

Dr                 **Prepayments Account**                 Cr

| Details | Amount | Details | Amount |
|---------|--------|---------|--------|
|         | £      |         | £      |
|         |        |         |        |

Dr                 **Van Account**                 Cr

| Details | Amount | Details | Amount |
|---------|--------|---------|--------|
|         | £      |         | £      |
| Balance b/d | 10,000 |     |        |
|         |        |         |        |

Dr                 **Depreciation Account**                 Cr

| Details | Amount | Details | Amount |
|---------|--------|---------|--------|
|         | £      |         | £      |
|         |        |         |        |

Dr       **Provision for Depreciation Account – Vans**       Cr

| Details | Amount | Details | Amount |
|---------|--------|---------|--------|
|         | £      |             | £     |
|         |        | Balance b/d | 6,000 |

Dr              **General Expenses Account**              Cr

| Details     | Amount | Details | Amount |
|-------------|--------|---------|--------|
|             | £      |         | £      |
| Balance b/d | 110    |         |        |

Dr                              **Assistant's Wages Account**                          Cr

| Details | Amount | Details | Amount |
|---------|--------|---------|--------|
|         | £      |         | £      |
|         |        |         |        |

Dr                                     **Accruals Account**                               Cr

| Details | Amount | Details | Amount |
|---------|--------|---------|--------|
|         | £      |         | £      |
|         |        |         |        |

Dr                                     **Debtor's Account**                               Cr

| Details | Amount | Details | Amount |
|---------|--------|---------|--------|
|         | £      |         | £      |
| Balance b/d | 4,120 |     |        |

Dr                               **Creditor's Account**                          Cr

| Details | Amount | Details | Amount |
|---------|--------|---------|--------|
|         | £      | Balance b/d | £ 2,250 |

Dr                               **Drawings Account**                           Cr

| Details | Amount | Details | Amount |
|---------|--------|---------|--------|
|         | £      |         | £      |

Dr                             **Materials Used Account**                        Cr

| Details | Amount | Details | Amount |
|---------|--------|---------|--------|
| Balance b/d  (opening stock) | £ 1,050 |         | £      |

| Dr | **Bad Debts Written Off Account** | | | Cr |
|---|---|---|---|---|
| Details | Amount | Details | | Amount |
| | £ | | | £ |
| | | | | |
| | | | | |
| | | | | |
| | | | | |

**12.4** The following figures are extracted from the accounts of Wyvern Systems Limited for the year ended 30 June 1999:

- sales for the year, £300,000

- opening stock, £20,000

- closing stock, £40,000

- purchases for the year, £260,000

**You are to calculate:**

(a)    cost of sales for the year

(b)    gross profit for the year

(c)    gross profit percentage mark up

(d)    gross profit percentage margin

**12.5** Talib Zabbar owns a shop selling children's clothes. He is convinced that one of his employees is stealing goods from the shop. He asks you to calculate from the accounting records the value of stock stolen.

The following information is available:

- sales for the year, £160,000

- opening stock at the beginning of the year, £30,500

- purchases for the year, £89,500

- closing stock at the end of the year, £21,500

- the gross profit margin achieved on all sales is 40 per cent

**You are to** calculate the value of stock stolen (if any) during the year.

Note: a pro-forma photocopiable extended trial balance is printed in the Appendix.

# 13 CLUB AND SOCIETY ACCOUNTS

**13.1** A club's income and expenditure account is:

(a)    the equivalent of a business' profit and loss account

(b)    the equivalent of a business' balance sheet

(c)    a summarised cash and bank account

(d)    a trial balance of the club

Answer (a) or (b) or (c) or (d)

**13.2** For the Wyevale Walking Club, members' subscriptions of £30 were overdue at the beginning of the year. £2,020 was received during the year, including the overdue amount and £18 for subscriptions in advance for the following year. What amount of subscription income will be recorded in this year's accounts?

(a)    £2,068

(b)    £2,038

(c)    £2,008

(d)    £1,972

Answer (a) or (b) or (c) or (d)

**13.3** The following information is available to the treasurer of Ryton Racquets Club for the year ended 31 December 1998:

| 1 January | Subscriptions prepaid | £450 |
|---|---|---|
| | Subscriptions owing | £1,275 |
| 31 December | Subscriptions received during the year | £15,600 |
| | Subscriptions prepaid for 1999 | £525 |
| | Subscriptions owing for 1998 | £1,500 |

Note: all subscriptions due at 1 January 1998 have now been paid and are included in the receipts for the year.

**You are to** calculate the amount of subscription income to be shown in the income and expenditure account for the year ended 31 December 1998.

**13.4** The treasurer of the Southmead Social Club has prepared the following receipts and payments account:

### RECEIPTS AND PAYMENTS ACCOUNT

### for the year ended 31 December 1999

| RECEIPTS | £ | PAYMENTS | £ |
|---|---|---|---|
| Balance b/d | 285 | Secretary's expenses | 2,215 |
| Subscriptions | 11,295 | Rent of premises | 4,000 |
| Competition fees | 620 | Printing and postages | 1,630 |
| Bank loan | 1,000 | Furniture and equipment | 3,250 |
| Drinks machine receipts | 1,222 | Loss on coach trip | 425 |
| | | Cleaner's wages | 2,100 |
| | | Sundry expenses | 550 |
| | | Balance c/d | 252 |
| | 14,422 | | 14,422 |

Additional information:
* at 1 January 1999, furniture and equipment was valued at £2,100; at 31 December 1999 it was valued at £4,500
* subscription receipts include·
  - £55 due from 1998
  - £70 paid in advance for 2000
* at 31 December 1999, subscriptions due but unpaid total £105
* the secretary held stocks of postage stamps as follows:
  - at 1 January 1999, £100
  - at 31 December 1999, £150
* at 31 December 1999 the cleaner was owed wages of £95

**You are to** prepare the figures for the income and expenditure account and balance sheet of the Southmead Social Club for the year ended 31 December 1999, using the extended trial balance method.

**13.5** The assets and liabilities of the Temeside Sports Club as at 1 January 1999 were:

- bank balance, £850

- furniture and equipment, £5,500

- bar stock, £2,045

- rent owing, £350

For the year ended 31 December 1999, the treasurer prepared the following receipts and payments account:

### RECEIPTS AND PAYMENTS ACCOUNT

### for the year ended 31 December 1999

| RECEIPTS | £ | PAYMENTS | £ |
|---|---|---|---|
| Balance b/d | 850 | Bar purchases | 9,355 |
| Subscriptions | 15,210 | Christmas Fayre expenses | 1,410 |
| Bar takings | 19,840 | Secretary's expenses | 2,109 |
| Christmas Fayre receipts | 4,090 | Wages | 16,110 |
| | | Rent | 5,200 |
| | | Furniture and equipment | 4,500 |
| | | Balance c/d | 1,306 |
| | 39,990 | | 39,990 |

Additional information at 31 December 1999:

- bar stock is valued at £2,980

- furniture and equipment is valued at £7,500

- subscriptions owing for 1999, £320

- subscriptions prepaid for next year, £550

- wages owing £310

**You are to** prepare the figures for the income and expenditure account and balance sheet of the Temeside Sports Club for the year ended 31 December 1999, using the extended trial balance method.

**13.6** The treasurer of the Perham Performing Arts Society has prepared the following receipts and payments account:

### RECEIPTS AND PAYMENTS ACCOUNT
### for the year ended 30 June 1999

| RECEIPTS | £ | PAYMENTS | £ |
|---|---|---|---|
| Balance b/d | 625 | Hire of hall | 4,110 |
| Subscriptions | 2,100 | Purchase of refreshments | 1,145 |
| Box office takings | 8,955 | Performing rights payments | 1,950 |
| Refreshment sales | 2,980 | Sundry expenses | 1,210 |
| | | Lighting and costumes | 5,380 |
| | | Balance c/d | 865 |
| | 14,660 | | 14,660 |

Lighting and costumes are treated as fixed assets; they are depreciated at 25 per cent of the written down value brought forward, together with additions during the year.

Additional information:

| | at 1 July 1998 | at 30 June 1999 |
|---|---|---|
| | £ | £ |
| • subscriptions owing | 55 | 85 |
| • subscriptions prepaid | 210 | 190 |
| • accrual for purchase of refreshments | 100 | 50 |
| • prepayment of hire of hall | – | 200 |
| • lighting and costumes (written down value) | 10,300 | to be calculated |

**You are to** prepare the figures for the income and expenditure account and balance sheet of the Perham Performing Arts Society for the year ended 30 June 1999, using the extended trial balance method.

Note: a pro-forma photocopiable extended trial balance is printed in the Appendix.

# 14 PARTNERSHIP ACCOUNTS

**14.1** Mike and Bernie are in partnership as 'M & B Builders'. The following figures are extracted from their accounts for the year ended 31 December 1999:

|  | £ |  |
| --- | --- | --- |
| **Capital accounts at 1 January 1999:** | | |
| Mike | 30,000 | Cr |
| Bernie | 20,000 | Cr |
| | | |
| **Current accounts at 1 January 1999:** | | |
| Mike | 1,560 | Cr |
| Bernie | 420 | Dr |
| | | |
| **Drawings for the year:** | | |
| Mike | 21,750 | |
| Bernie | 17,350 | |
| | | |
| **Partnership salary:** | | |
| Bernie | 7,500 | |
| | | |
| **Interest on capital for the year:** | | |
| Mike | 1,500 | |
| Bernie | 1,000 | |
| | | |
| **Share of profits for the year:** | | |
| Mike | 20,200 | |
| Bernie | 10,100 | |

Note: there is no interest charged on drawings

**You are to** show the partners' capital and current accounts for the year ended 31 December 1999.

**14.2** Clark and Pearce are in partnership selling business computer systems. The following trial balance has been taken from their accounts for the year ended 30 June 1999, after the calculation of gross profit:

|  | Dr | Cr |
|---|---|---|
|  | £ | £ |
| Gross profit |  | 105,000 |
| Salaries | 30,400 |  |
| Electricity | 2,420 |  |
| Telephone | 3,110 |  |
| Rent and rates | 10,000 |  |
| Discount allowed | 140 |  |
| Office expenses | 10,610 |  |
| *Stock at 30 June 1999 | 41,570 |  |
| Debtors and creditors | 20,000 | 6,950 |
| Value Added Tax |  | 5,240 |
| Bad debts written off | 1,200 |  |
| Provision for bad debts |  | 780 |
| Office equipment at cost | 52,000 |  |
| Provision for depreciation on office equipment |  | 20,800 |
| Clark: Capital account |  | 60,000 |
| Current account |  | 430 |
| Drawings | 20,600 |  |
| Pearce: Capital account |  | 30,000 |
| Current account |  | 300 |
| Drawings | 15,700 |  |
| Bank | 21,750 |  |
|  | 229,500 | 229,500 |

\* Closing stock is included in the trial balance because gross profit for the year has been calculated already.

*Notes:*
- profits and losses are shared as follows: Clark two-thirds, Pearce one-third
- depreciate the office equipment at 20 per cent, using the straight line method

**You are to** prepare the figures for the partnership final accounts for the year ended 30 June 1999, using the extended trial balance method.

**14.3** Sara and Simon Penny are in partnership running a catering service called 'Class Caterers'. The following trial balance has been taken from their accounts for the year ended 31 March 1999:

|  | Dr £ | Cr £ |
|---|---|---|
| Capital accounts: |  |  |
| Sara |  | 10,000 |
| Simon |  | 6,000 |
| Current accounts: |  |  |
| Sara |  | 560 |
| Simon |  | 1,050 |
| Drawings: |  |  |
| Sara | 12,700 |  |
| Simon | 7,400 |  |
| Purchases | 11,300 |  |
| Sales |  | 44,080 |
| Stock at 1 April 1998 | 2,850 |  |
| Wages | 8,020 |  |
| Rent and rates | 4,090 |  |
| Sundry expenses | 1,390 |  |
| Equipment | 8,000 |  |
| Debtors | 4,500 |  |
| Creditors |  | 5,850 |
| Value Added Tax |  | 1,350 |
| Bank | 8,640 |  |
|  | 68,890 | 68,890 |

*Notes at 31 March 1999:*

• stock was valued at £3,460

• sundry expenses owing, £110

• depreciation is to be charged on the equipment at 10% per year

• profits and losses are to be shared equally

**You are to:**

(a) prepare the partnership final accounts for the year ended 31 March 1999, using the extended trial balance method

(b) show the partners' capital and current accounts for the year

**14.4** Anne Adams and Jenny Beeson are partners in an electrical supplies shop called 'A & B Electrics'. They share profits and losses equally. The following trial balance has been taken from their accounts for the year ended 30 June 1999:

|  |  | Dr | Cr |
|---|---|---:|---:|
|  |  | £ | £ |
| Capital accounts: | A Adams |  | 30,000 |
|  | J Beeson |  | 20,000 |
| Current accounts: | A Adams |  | 780 |
|  | J Beeson |  | 920 |
| Drawings: | A Adams | 14,000 |  |
|  | J Beeson | 12,000 |  |
| Stock at 1 July 1998 |  | 26,550 |  |
| Purchases and sales |  | 175,290 | 250,140 |
| Returns |  | 1,360 | 850 |
| Rent and rates |  | 8,420 |  |
| Wages |  | 28,700 |  |
| Motor vehicle expenses |  | 2,470 |  |
| General expenses |  | 6,210 |  |
| Motor vehicle at cost |  | 12,000 |  |
| Fixtures and fittings at cost |  | 4,000 |  |
| Provision for depreciation: | motor vehicle |  | 3,000 |
|  | fixtures and fittings |  | 800 |
| Debtors and creditors |  | 6,850 | 12,360 |
| Value Added Tax |  |  | 2,410 |
| Bank |  | 22,009 |  |
| Cash |  | 1,376 |  |
| Bad debts written off |  | 175 |  |
| Provision for bad debts |  |  | 150 |
|  |  | 321,410 | 321,410 |

*Notes at 30 June 1999:*
- stock is valued at £27,750
- rates paid in advance £250
- wages owing £320
- provision for bad debts to be equal to 2 per cent debtors
- depreciation on fixtures and fittings to be provided at 10 per cent per annum using the straight line method
- depreciation on motor vehicles to be provided at 25 per cent per annum using the reducing balance method

**You are to:**
(a) prepare the partnership final accounts for the year ended 30 June 1999, using the extended trial balance method
(b) show the partners' capital and current accounts for the year

# 15 MANUFACTURING ACCOUNTS

**15.1** In a manufacturing business, the hire cost of specialist machinery to carry out a particular manufacturing task is included under the heading of:

(a)    direct materials

(b)    direct expenses

(c)    production overheads

(d)    non-production overheads

Answer (a) or (b) or (c) or (d)

**15.2** The following figures relate to Crown Heath Manufacturing Company for the year ended 31 December 1998:

|  | £ |
|---|---|
| Stock at 1 January 1998: | |
| Raw materials | 11,000 |
| Finished goods | 5,500 |
| Stock at 31 December 1998: | |
| Raw materials | 12,500 |
| Finished goods | 4,750 |
| Expenditure during year: | |
| Purchases of raw materials | 33,850 |
| Factory wages – direct | 35,210 |
| Factory wages – indirect | 24,840 |
| Factory rent and rates | 12,500 |
| Factory power | 4,300 |
| Depreciation of factory machinery | 2,100 |
| Factory insurance | 450 |
| Sundry factory expenses | 500 |
| Sales during year | 145,000 |

Note: factory power is to be treated as a production overhead.

You are to prepare year-end accounts which show clearly:

- cost of raw materials used
- prime cost
- cost of goods completed
- cost of sales
- gross profit for the year

**15.3** The following figures relate to Martley Manufacturing for the year ended 31 December 1999:

| | £ |
|---|---|
| Stock at 1 January 1999: | |
| Raw materials | 105,000 |
| Work-in-progress | 24,000 |
| Finished goods | 43,000 |
| Stock at 31 December 1999: | |
| Raw materials | 102,000 |
| Work-in-progress | 29,000 |
| Finished goods | 32,000 |
| Expenditure during year: | |
| Purchases of raw materials | 272,000 |
| Direct factory wages | 126,000 |
| Rent and rates | 12,000 |
| Factory power | 20,000 |
| Depreciation of factory machinery | 9,000 |
| Repairs to factory buildings | 3,000 |
| Sundry factory expenses | 9,000 |
| Indirect wages and salaries | 84,000 |
| Advertising | 38,000 |
| Office expenses | 31,000 |
| Depreciation of office equipment | 7,500 |
| Sales during year | 704,000 |

*Additional information:*
- factory power is to be treated as a production overhead
- indirect wages and salaries owing at year-end £4,000
- indirect wages and salaries to be allocated 50% to manufacturing and 50% to administration
- rent and rates to be allocated 75% to manufacturing and 25% to administration
- office expenses prepaid at year-end £2,000
- goods completed are transferred to profit and loss account at production cost plus ten per cent factory profit
- the finished goods stocks are shown at cost price

**You are to** prepare manufacturing and profit and loss accounts for the year ended 31 December 1999, to show clearly:
- cost of raw materials used
- prime cost
- total of production (factory) overheads
- production cost of goods completed
- cost of sales
- gross profit for the year
- net profit for the year

**15.4** Nick Patel has recently started in business making top quality 'executive' desks for office and home use. His first month's costs were:

|  |  | £ |
|---|---|---:|
| • | direct materials used | 2,410 |
| • | direct labour | 3,840 |
| • | production overheads | 1,065 |
| • | non-production overheads | 825 |

At the end of the first month he has completed fifty desks and there are ten desks which are exactly half-finished as regards direct materials, direct labour and production overheads. No sales have yet been made as Nick needs to build up a stock before he commences his advertising campaign.

Nick estimates that the net realisable value of each completed desk is £250. At the end of the month, the business holds stocks of raw materials as follows:

|  | cost | net realisable value |
|---|---:|---:|
|  | £ | £ |
| Material A | 850 | 950 |
| Material B | 590 | 700 |
| Material C | 700 | 650 |

**You are to** calculate the month end stock valuation for:

- raw materials
- work-in-progress
- finished goods

**15.5** A manufacturer values the closing stock of finished goods at factory cost plus 25 per cent. For 1999 the opening and closing stocks (including factory profit of 25 per cent) were £20,000 and £15,000 respectively. Show the transactions on provision for unrealised profit account for the year ended 31 December 1999.

Note: a pro-forma photocopiable asset register is printed in the Appendix.

# 16 ACCOUNTING FOR CAPITAL TRANSACTIONS

**16.1** Which one of the following is an intangible fixed asset?

(a)  vehicles

(b)  development costs

(c)  hire purchase

(d)  premises

Answer (a) or (b) or (c) or (d)


**16.2** Eveshore Enterprises is considering the use of hire purchase as a means of financing a new computer. Which of the following statements is correct?

(a)  at the end of the hire purchase contract, ownership of the computer will pass from the finance company to Eveshore Enterprises

(b)  a hire purchase contract is the same as an operating lease

(c)  at the end of the hire purchase contract, the finance company will collect the computer from Eveshore Enterprises

(d)  as the computer is being financed through hire purchase, it is not recorded on the balance sheet of Eveshore Enterprises

Answer (a) or (b) or (c) or (d)


**16.3** Which one of the following is the least likely source of finance for major long-term capital expenditure?

(a)  finance lease

(b)  hire purchase

(c)  capital/share issue

(d)  bank overdraft

Answer (a) or (b) or (c) or (d)


**16.4**  (a)  An extract from the fixed asset register of Mereford Manufacturing is shown on the next page. You are to update the register with depreciation on the fixed asset for the years ended 31 December 1998 and 1999.

(b)  The fixed asset is sold on 20 April 2000 for £600 (net of VAT). The company does not charge depreciation in the year of sale. You are to complete the fixed asset register showing the profit or loss on sale.

**FIXED ASSET RECORD**

| No | 5423 |
|---|---|
| **Description** | Moulding machine MM500 |
| **Location** | Factory |
| **Supplier** | Middleton Machines Limited |

| Date | Cost (net of VAT) £ | Expected useful life | Estimated scrap value £ | Depreciation method SL or RB | Percentage per annum | Depreciation for year £ | Provision for dep'n £ | Net book value £ | Disposal proceeds (net of VAT) £ | Profit/loss on sale £ |
|---|---|---|---|---|---|---|---|---|---|---|
| **1996** | | | | | | | | | | |
| 7 Feb | 10,000 | 5 years | nil | SL | 20% | | | | | |
| 31 Dec | | | | | | 2,000 | 2,000 | 8,000 | | |
| **1997** | | | | | | | | | | |
| 31 Dec | | | | | | 2,000 | 4,000 | 6,000 | | |

**16.5** Perham Publishing, which has a financial year end of 31 December, bought a colour laser printer on 11 February 1998 at a cost of £2,000 (paid by cheque). The printer is expected to last for four years, after which its estimated value will be £260. Depreciation is charged at 40 per cent each year using the reducing balance method; it is charged in full in the year of purchase, but not in the year of sale.

The printer is part-exchanged for a more up-to-date model on 19 October 2000. The part-exchange allowance is £400.

**You are to**

(a) show the accounting entries (journal and cash book not required) to record the acquisition, depreciation and disposal of the printer for the years 1998, 1999, 2000.

*Note: VAT is to be ignored*

(b) draw up a page from the fixed asset register to show the printer's acquisition, depreciation and disposal. (A photocopiable page from the fixed asset register is provided in the Appendix).

**16.6** John and Sara Smith run a delivery company called 'J & S Transport'. They started in business on 1 January 1998 with two vans which cost £16,000 each (paid by cheque). On 1 January 2000, a further two vans were bought at a cost of £18,000 each (paid by cheque) and, on 20 March 2000, one of the original vans was sold for £8,000 (cheque received).

Depreciation is charged at 25 per cent each year using the reducing balance method; depreciation is charged in the year of purchase, but none in the year of sale.

The Smith's financial year end is 31 December.

You are to show the accounting entries (journal and cash book not required) to record the acquisition, depreciation and disposal of vans for the years 1998, 1999 and 2000.

*Notes:*

- VAT is to be ignored
- use one fixed asset account for all vans, one depreciation account and one provision for depreciation account

**16.7** Axis Agrochemicals Limited has the following revenue expenditure for the year ended 30 June 1999:

- pure research               £50,000
- applied research      £40,000
- development          £80,000

The development expenditure relates to a new product 'Weedex QT' which has been on sale since July 1999. Early indications show that the product is selling well and the marketing department is confident that it will have a product life of at least four years.

You are to explain how each of the above items should be accounted for in the company's year end accounts in order to comply with standard accounting practice. Note any alternative permissible accounting treatments, and demonstrate their effect on profit in the year ended 30 June 1999 and in future years.

**16.8** (a) Write short notes, distinguishing between:

- an operating lease
- a finance lease

(b) Explain the accounting treatment of each of these types of lease in the accounts of the lessee (the person to whom the asset is leased).

# Assignments

This section contains six assignments – sets of extended activities which consolidate learning and prepare the student for assessment.

## ASSIGNMENTS

1      James Belushi – incomplete records

2      Andy Gillman – extended trial balance

3      Adcock & Tweed – accruals, prepayments and club accounts

4      Hillview Leisure – dealing with capital transactions

5      Marston & Banks – manufacturing accounts and partnerships

6      Bon Voyage – bank reconciliations and control accounts

Coverage of the NVQ specifications is set out at the beginning of each assignment.

# ASSIGNMENT
# JAMES BELUSHI – INCOMPLETE RECORDS

*1*

## PERFORMANCE CRITERIA COVERED

The following performance criteria are covered by this assignment:

**Element 4.2: Record income and expenditure**

i       All income and expenditure is correctly identified and recorded in the appropriate records.

ii      Relevant accrued and prepaid income and expenditure is correctly identified and adjustments made.

iv      Incomplete data is identified and either resolved or referred to the appropriate person.

**Element 4.3: Collect and collate information for the preparation of final accounts.**

i       Relevant accounts and reconciliations are correctly prepared to allow the preparation of final accounts.

ii      All relevant information is correctly identified and recorded.

iii     Investigations into business transactions are conducted with tact and courtesy.

iv      The organisation's policies, regulations, procedures and timescales relating to the preparation of final accounts are observed.

v       Discrepancies and unusual features are identified and either resolved or referred to the appropriate person.

# THE SITUATION

James Belushi is in the confectionery packaging business. He purchases paper and cardboard and converts these items into chocolate boxes which he sells to the sweet manufacturing industry. He operates from a warehouse in Leigh Sinton but most of the boxes are folded and packaged by a series of outworkers who work from home. James does not maintain a full set of accounting records but the following list of balances has been supplied; they relate to the start and end of his current financial year.

| JAMES BELUSHI: ACCOUNT BALANCES | 1st May 1998 | 30th April 1999 |
|---|---|---|
| | £ | £ |
| Warehouse at Cost | 80,000 | 80,000 |
| Motor Van (Cost £22,000) | 16,500 | 12,375 |
| Warehouse Machinery (Cost £16,000) | 12,000 | 9,000 |
| Stock at Cost | 6,250 | 7,490 |
| Trade Debtors | 8,370 | 10,420 |
| Prepayments | | |
| Motor Van Expenses | 400 | 375 |
| Business Insurances | 150 | 225 |
| Unified Business Rates | 260 | 650 |
| Cash at Bank | 7,250 | 5,880 |
| Cash in Hand | 250 | 400 |
| Trade Creditors | 9,330 | 8,670 |
| Accruals | | |
| Heat and Light | 750 | 590 |
| Telephone | 180 | 410 |
| Wages | 3,150 | 4,660 |

Mr Belushi maintains the bank account and cash account himself. He has provided you with the summarised Cash Book shown on the next page.

The cash book has been balanced and agreed to the bank statements and the new cash float.

---

**JAMES BELUSHI – CASH BOOK SUMMARY**

| RECEIPTS | CASH | BANK |
|---|---|---|
| | £ | £ |
| Balances brought down | 250 | 7,250 |
| Cash sales | 13,400 | 8,600 |
| Receipts from customers | 2,890 | 157,750 |
| Cash banked | - | 8,250 |
| | | |
| TOTAL | 16,540 | 181,850 |

| PAYMENTS | CASH | BANK |
|---|---|---|
| | £ | £ |
| Cash purchases | 1,970 | - |
| Drawings | 1,900 | 28,590 |
| General expenses | 350 | 3,110 |
| Telephone | - | 2,850 |
| Wages | 2,480 | 24,660 |
| Cash banked | 8,250 | - |
| Paid to suppliers | - | 82,370 |
| Heat and light | - | 4,330 |
| Motor van expenses | 960 | 8,440 |
| Business insurances | - | 11,120 |
| Business Rates | - | 7,140 |
| Advertising | - | 2,400 |
| Machine repairs | 230 | 960 |
| Balances c/d | 400 | 5,880 |
| | | |
| TOTAL | 16,540 | 181,850 |

## TASKS

1      Calculate the opening capital balance as at 1st May 1998, using the statement of affairs on the next page.

2      Calculate the figure for credit sales for the year. You may use the pro-forma debtors control account on page 76.

3    Calculate the figure for credit purchases for the year. You may use the pro-forma creditors control account on page 76.

4    Prepare a Trading, Profit and Loss account for the year to 30 April 1999 in the vertical format. You may use the pro-forma provided on page 77.

5    Prepare a balance sheet as at 30 April 1999. You may use the pro-forma balance sheet provided on page 78.

6    When Mr Belushi submitted the books to you he says that he has worked out that he has made a loss this year. He has concluded this from the fact that his business bank account went down from £7,250 to £5,880 during the year and this is a good indicator with regard to profitability.

Respond to Mr Belushi's comments on the memorandum on page 79. You should make specific reference to the accounting concepts that you think are relevant in the calculation of profit. Use your own name and the title of accounts assistant.

---

## STATEMENT OF AFFAIRS

|  | assets £ | liabilities £ |
|---|---|---|

**DEBTORS' CONTROL ACCOUNT**

Dr                                                                                                Cr

| Date | Details | Amount | Date | Details | Amount |
|------|---------|--------|------|---------|--------|
|      |         | £      |      |         | £      |
|      |         |        |      |         |        |

**CREDITORS' CONTROL ACCOUNT**

Dr                                                                                                Cr

| Date | Details | Amount | Date | Details | Amount |
|------|---------|--------|------|---------|--------|
|      |         | £      |      |         | £      |
|      |         |        |      |         |        |

**JAMES BELUSHI**

**TRADING, PROFIT AND LOSS ACCOUNT FOR THE YEAR TO** ................................

|  | £ | £ | £ |
|---|---|---|---|
| Cash Sales | | | |
| Credit Sales | | | |
| | | | |
| **Cost of Sales** | | | |
| Opening Stock | | | |
| Cash Purchases | | | |
| Credit Purchases | | | |
| | | | |
| | | | |
| *less* Closing Stock | | | |
| | | | |
| **Gross Profit** | | | |
| **Expenditure** | | | |
| General expenses | | | |
| Telephone | | | |
| Wages | | | |
| Heat and Light | | | |
| Motor van expenses | | | |
| Business Insurances | | | |
| Business Rates | | | |
| Advertising | | | |
| Machine repairs | | | |
| Depreciation: | | | |
|     Motor van | | | |
|     Machinery | | | |
| | | | |
| **Net Profit/ (Loss) for the year** | | | |

## JAMES BELUSHI
## BALANCE SHEET AS AT .................................................

| | Cost | Depreciation to date | Net |
|---|---|---|---|
| | £ | £ | £ |

**FIXED ASSETS**

Warehouse

Motor Van

Warehouse Machinery

**CURRENT ASSETS**

Stock

Debtors

Prepayments

Cash at Bank

Cash in Hand

**CURRENT LIABILITIES**

Trade Creditors

Accruals

**NET CURRENT ASSETS**

**REPRESENTED BY:**

CAPITAL

Balance at 1 May 1998

Add Net Profit for the year

Less Drawings

# MEMORANDUM

**To:**

**From:**

**Subject:**                                        **Date:**

# ASSIGNMENT
# ANDY GILLMAN – EXTENDED TRIAL BALANCE

2

## PERFORMANCE CRITERIA COVERED

The following performance criteria are covered by this assignment:

### Element 4.1: Maintain records and accounts relating to capital expenditure

iv    Depreciation charges and other necessary entries and adjustments are correctly calculated and recorded in the appropriate ledger records.

### Element 4.2: Record income and expenditure

i    All income and expenditure is correctly recorded in the appropriate records.

ii    Relevant accrued or prepaid income and expenditure is correctly identified and adjustments are made.

iv    Incomplete data is identified and either resolved or referred to the appropriate person.

### Element 4.4: Prepare the extended trial balance

i    Totals from the general ledger or other records are correctly entered on the extended trial balance.

ii    Material errors disclosed by the trial balance are identified, traced and referred to the appropriate authority.

iii    Adjustments not dealt with in the ledger accounts are correctly entered on the extended trial balance.

iv    An agreed valuation of closing stock is correctly entered on the extended trial balance.

vii    The extended trial balance is accurately extended and totalled.

## THE SITUATION

Andy Gillman is a sole trader who buys and sells recorded music from a shop in the High Street. The majority of his sales are for cash, although some credit is extended to the local disc jockeys in the area.

Andy has some knowledge of accounting but his latest trial balance does not agree, and the difference has been posted to a suspense account.

Upon investigation the following errors have been discovered:

- An error of transposition has taken place in the motor expenses account. The total for this account should read as £1,530 instead of its brought down figure of £1,350.

- A second-hand computer was bought during the year to assist with the office procedures as well as introducing some system of stock control. Its cost of £500 has currently been analysed to purchases.

- A payment made to a local nightclub for advertising has been credited to the bank account for £98, but no corresponding entry has been made.

- A credit note for £120 received from a supplier for goods returned has been debited to the supplier's account, but again no other entry has been made.

- Finally, a payment totalling £150 made for the purchase of CDs has been credited to the bank account but then inadvertently credited again to the sales account.

## TASKS

1    Provide journal entries for the errors listed above in order to clear the suspense account. You can use the journal layout provided on page 83.  Note that narratives are not required.

2    Further adjustments are required in order to complete the accounts.

Depreciation rates are calculated using the straight line method based on cost and are as follows:

| | |
|---|---|
| Motor Vehicles | 25% |
| Buildings | 5% |
| Fixtures and fittings | 20% |
| Office Equipment | 20% |

Disc Jockeys are notoriously bad payers and are quite likely to move on or disappear without any notice. The provision for bad debts should therefore be maintained at 10% of the closing debtors figure  at all times.

Closing stock is valued at cost at £4,350, but there are some Acid Jazz CDs which are proving hard to sell. The consignment originally cost £460 but will have to be marked down as a sale item and sold for £300 in total.

Other adjustments relating to year end procedures are as follows:

**Accrued expenditure as at 31 January 1999**

| | |
|---|---|
| Light and Heat | £50 |
| Salaries and Wages | £70 |
| General Expenses | £20 |

**Prepaid expenses as at 31 January 1999**

| | |
|---|---|
| Rates | £50 |
| Insurance | £90 |
| Motor Expenses | £110 |

You are required to prepare an extended trial balance for Andy Gillman for the year to 31 January 1999. Use the pro-forma on pages 84 and 85.

3    Write a brief memo to Andy Gillman explaining why the stock valuation at the end of January 1999 was adjusted. You should refer to the relevant accounting standards and accounting concepts. Use the memorandum form on page 86.

| JOURNAL | | |
|---|---|---|
| Details | Dr £ | Cr £ |
| | | |
| | | |
| | | |
| | | |
| | | |

# ANDY GILLMAN – EXTENDED TRIAL BALANCE

| account name | ledger balances | |
|---|---|---|
| | Dr £ | Cr £ |
| Sales turnover | | 42,500 |
| Purchases | 20,750 | |
| Salaries & Wages | 1,500 | |
| Motor Expenses | 1,350 | |
| Rates | 1,010 | |
| Light and Heat | 695 | |
| Cleaning and Maintenance costs | 425 | |
| Advertising | 360 | |
| Stock | 2,150 | |
| Trade Debtors | 2,050 | |
| Provision for Doubtful Debts | | 316 |
| Decrease in Provision for Doubtful Debts | | |
| Cash in Hand | 100 | |
| Cash in Bank | 650 | |
| Trade Creditors | | 4,350 |
| Bank Loan | | 5,000 |
| Buildings (Cost) | 50,000 | |
| Fixtures and Fittings (Cost) | 2,500 | |
| Motor Vehicles (Cost) | 8,000 | |
| Office Equipment (Cost) | 1,500 | |
| Buildings: Provision for Depreciation | | 5,000 |
| Fixtures & Fittings: Provision for Depreciation | | 750 |
| Motor Vehicles: Provision for Depreciation | | 4,000 |
| Office Equipment: Provision for Depreciation | | 150 |
| Depreciation - Buildings | | |
| Depreciation - Fixtures & Fittings | | |
| Depreciation - Motor Vehicles | | |
| Depreciation - Office Equipment | | |
| Returns Inwards | 450 | |
| Drawings | 12,000 | |
| Returns Outwards | | 690 |
| General Expenses | 965 | |
| Insurance | 1,225 | |
| Loan interest payable | 168 | |
| Accruals | | |
| Prepayments | | |
| Capital | | 45,550 |
| Suspense A/C | 458 | |
| Profit / ( loss ) for the year | | |
| | 108,306 | 108,306 |

| adjustments | | profit and loss | | balance sheet | |
|---|---|---|---|---|---|
| Dr £ | Cr £ | Dr £ | Cr £ | Dr £ | Cr £ |
| | | | | | |
| | | | | | |
| | | | | | |
| | | | | | |
| | | | | | |
| | | | | | |
| | | | | | |
| | | | | | |
| | | | | | |
| | | | | | |
| | | | | | |
| | | | | | |
| | | | | | |
| | | | | | |
| | | | | | |
| | | | | | |
| | | | | | |
| | | | | | |
| | | | | | |
| | | | | | |
| | | | | | |
| | | | | | |
| | | | | | |
| | | | | | |
| | | | | | |
| | | | | | |
| | | | | | |
| | | | | | |
| | | | | | |
| | | | | | |
| | | | | | |
| | | | | | |
| | | | | | |
| | | | | | |
| | | | | | |
| | | | | | |
| | | | | | |
| | | | | | |

# MEMORANDUM

**To:**

**From:**

**Subject:**                                              **Date:**

# ASSIGNMENT: ADCOCK & TWEED – ACCRUALS, PREPAYMENTS & CLUB ACCOUNTS

*3*

## PERFORMANCE CRITERIA COVERED

The following performance criteria are covered by this assignment:

### Element 4.2  Record income and expenditure

i       All income and expenditure is correctly identified and recorded in the appropriate records.

ii      Relevant accrued or prepaid income and expenditure is correctly identified and adjustments are made.

iii     The organisation's policies, regulations, procedures and timescales in relation to recording income and expenditure are observed.

iv      Incomplete data is identified and either resolved or referred to the appropriate person.

### Element 4.3  Collect and collate information for the preparation of final accounts

i       Relevant accounts and reconciliations are correctly prepared to allow the preparation of final accounts.

ii      All relevant information is correctly identified and recorded.

iii     Investigations into business transactions are conducted with tact and courtesy.

iv      The organisation's policies, regulations, procedures and timescales relating to preparing final accounts are observed.

v       Discrepancies and unusual features are identified and either resolved or referred to the appropriate person.

# THE SITUATION

You are employed by a firm of Accountants, Adcock and Tweed, as a trainee. Your duties are quite varied; they include the preparation of final accounts in readiness for checking by the senior partner, Graham Adcock.

# SECTION 1 – ALAN PARTRIDGE

Today's date is 24 January 1999 and one of your clients, Alan Partridge, needs his year-end accounts adjusted for the relevant accruals and prepayments.

Mr Partridge runs a landscape and gardening business in Persham, operating from an industrial unit near the railway station. In this unit he stores his equipment and carries out repairs to mowers and other garden machinery. The address is Unit 16 Avon Industrial Estate, Persham, WR3 7YG.

Set out below is a list of the business expenditure which Mr Partridge has incurred during the year, together with details of opening and closing balances. Alan's accounting year-end is 31 October.

## HEAT AND LIGHT

At the start of the 1997/1998 financial year (1 November 1997) there was a balance of £546 outstanding on the electricity account.

During the year the business made the following payments on the dates stipulated:

|  |  | £ |
|---|---|---|
| 21.11.97 | by cheque | 827 |
| 24.02.98 | by cheque | 959 |
| 15.05.98 | by cash | 633 |
| 27.08.98 | by cash | 472 |

It has now been estimated by the electricity company that Mr Partridge owes a further £347 for the period to 31.10.98.

## ADVERTISING

Alan Partridge has an account with Yellow Pages to advertise in their classified section. He pays for this quarterly in advance. At 31 October 1997 Mr Partridge had already paid £600 in advance for the two months to December 1997. The agreement is renegotiated every six months.

During the year the business paid the following quarterly instalments:

|  |  | £ |
|---|---|---|
| 02.01.98 | by cheque (to March 1998) | 900 |
| 01.04.98 | by cheque (to June 1998) | 1,050 |
| 07.07.98 | by cheque (to Sept 1998) | 1,050 |
| 06.10.98 | by cheque (to Dec 1998) | 1,125 |

## TELEPHONE

Mr Partridge's telephone operates on the Mercury system and as part of their introductory offer to businesses in the area they are currently supplying the line rental free for the next two years. This means that businesses such as Alan's only pay for the calls made on the telephone line.

At the start of this accounting year it was estimated that Alan owed £214 for calls.

During the year the following quarterly payments were made:

|  |  | £ |
|---|---|---|
| 21.12.97 | by direct debit | 504 |
| 26.03.98 | by direct debit | 667 |
| 24.06.98 | by direct debit | 496 |
| 29.09.98 | by direct debit | 571 |

No details are available at present as to what calls have been made for the period 29.09.98 to 31.10.98, but looking at the previous quarter's bill and last year's accrual, you have estimated this to be £189.

## RENT RECEIVED

To provide valuable additional income to the business, Alan sub-lets the first-floor office part of the Industrial unit to another trader, Miss Susan Wilkinson, who uses it for her secretarial business 'Temps Galore'. As this name suggests, she provides temporary secretarial cover to businesses in the area.

The rental agreement has been fixed for a three year period to 31.12.2000 at £9,000 per annum. At the start of the current year (1 November 1997), Sue owed Alan one month's rent.

Unfortunately, throughout the year she proved rather unreliable with the quarterly payments and the following was received by Alan on the dates given:

|  |  | £ |
|---|---|---|
| 06.11.97 | cash | 1,500 |
| 03.03.98 | cash | 3,000 |
| 07.07.98 | cheque | 3,750 |
| 31.08.98 | credit transfer | 3,000 |

# SECTION 1 TASKS

**1.1**   Write up the nominal ledger accounts for Alan Partridge showing clearly the opening and closing balances, the amounts paid/received during the year as well as the transfers to be made to the profit and loss account. You can use the nominal accounts shown on pages 90 to 91.

**1.2**   Alan Partridge does not understand why he has to submit his books to you each year, to have them adjusted for the closing accruals and prepayments. After all this costs him money and after a period of time he reckons you could quite easily base the financial statements on the amounts paid and received during the year.

Respond to this comment of Alan's on the letterhead on page 97. Prepare your letter for Mr Adcock's signature. Your reply should mention the relevant accounting concepts and conventions.

Dr                  **HEAT AND LIGHT ACCOUNT**                  Cr

| Date | Details | Amount | Date | Details | Amount |
|------|---------|--------|------|---------|--------|
|      |         | £      |      |         | £      |
|      |         |        |      |         |        |

Dr                  **ADVERTISING ACCOUNT**                  Cr

| Date | Details | Amount | Date | Details | Amount |
|------|---------|--------|------|---------|--------|
|      |         | £      |      |         | £      |
|      |         |        |      |         |        |

Dr **TELEPHONE ACCOUNT** Cr

| Date | Details | Amount | Date | Details | Amount |
|------|---------|--------|------|---------|--------|
|      |         | £      |      |         | £      |
|      |         |        |      |         |        |

Dr **RENT RECEIVED ACCOUNT** Cr

| Date | Details | Amount | Date | Details | Amount |
|------|---------|--------|------|---------|--------|
|      |         | £      |      |         | £      |
|      |         |        |      |         |        |

# ADCOCK & TWEED, ACCOUNTANTS
29 Union Street

Eveshore

WR6 5HN

Tel 01905 748888 Fax 01905 748934 VAT Reg 234 2356 12

Graham Adcock FCCA, Jennifer Tweed ACCA

## SECTION 2 – RIVER WYE BOWLS CLUB

People knowing that you are an accounting trainee are always approaching you for free advice, to help them with their business. Even your friends are not slow to ask for your assistance; one of them, Kevin Francis, is Treasurer for the local Bowls club and he has volunteered your services to act as external Auditor and Accountant. The latest set of books and balances have been handed to you.

### THE RIVER WYE BOWLS CLUB

The following is a summary of the River Wye's Bowls Club's cash book for the year ended  30 November 1998.

| RECEIPTS | £ | PAYMENTS | £ |
|---|---|---|---|
| Bar sales | 14,567 | Rent on Clubhouse | 3,500 |
| Match fees | 444 | Rates | 1,700 |
| Members' subscriptions | 4,750 | Heat and Light | 996 |
| Donations received | 340 | Groundsman's Wages | 4,400 |
| Gaming Machine receipts | 4,220 | Printing & Stationery | 358 |
| Annual Dinner Dance receipts | 2,450 | Administration costs | 700 |
| | | Dinner Dance expenses | 2,960 |
| | | Secretaries expenses | 109 |
| | | Bar suppliers | 8,670 |
| | | New Roller | 540 |
| | | Bar staff wages | 2,875 |
| | | Gaming Machine rent | 1,440 |

Kevin is also able to give you the following information relating to balances that exist at the start and the end of the year.

| | 30 November 1997 £ | 30 November 1998 £ |
|---|---|---|
| Bar Supplier creditor | 1,560 | 1,945 |
| Accruals for Heat and Light | 135 | 186 |
| Prepaid Rates | 125 | 170 |
| Subscriptions in arrears | 250 | 200 |
| Subscriptions in advance | 50 | 75 |
| Bar stock | 1,210 | 1,575 |
| Cash at bank | 210 | to be calculated |
| Groundsmans Equipment at NBV | 6,224 | |
| Clubhouse Furniture at NBV | 3,400 | |

**ADDITIONAL INFORMATION**

It is the Bowls Club's policy to depreciate it's assets on the following basis:

|  | % |
|---|---|
| Groundsman's Equipment | 15 |
| Clubhouse Furniture | 10 |

All rates are based on the reduced balance method, ie on the book value brought forward from the previous year.

It is also policy that all charges for depreciation are rounded up to the nearest whole pound. The club charges a full year's depreciation in the year of acquisition irrespective of the actual date of purchase and no depreciation is taken in the year of sale.

# SECTION 2 TASKS

**2.1**   Construct an Income and Expenditure account for the year to 30 November 1998, calculating the surplus/deficit for the year. Use the format shown on the next page. If a deficit is involved, the total figure at the bottom is normally shown in brackets.

**2.2**   Prepare a balance sheet as at 30 November 1998, showing the Accumulated fund balance brought forward and carried forward. Use the format shown on page 96.

**2.3**   Kevin in his role as treasurer has just told you that at the recent Annual General Meeting the members are now discussing the possibility of offering a Life Membership next year. This will constitute a one-off payment in the region of £360, similar to that offered by the local County cricket club to its members.

Kevin, however, is unsure how this should be entered into the accounts. On the letterhead on page 97 explain to Kevin the correct accounting treatment available to the bowls club with regard to 'Life Membership.' Sign the letter in your own name. The date is 20 January 1999.

## THE RIVER WYE BOWLS CLUB

## INCOME AND EXPENDITURE ACCOUNT FOR THE YEAR TO 30 NOVEMBER 1998

**Income**  £  £

**Expenditure**

**Surplus/(Deficit) for the year**

**THE RIVER WYE BOWLS CLUB**
**BALANCE SHEET AS AT** ........................................

|  | £ | £ | £ |
|---|---|---|---|

FIXED ASSETS

CURRENT ASSETS

CURRENT LIABILITIES

NET CURRENT LIABILITIES

REPRESENTED BY:

# ADCOCK & TWEED, ACCOUNTANTS

29 Union Street

Eveshore

WR6 5HN

Tel 01905 748888 Fax 01905 748934 VAT Reg 234 2356 12

Graham Adcock FCCA, Jennifer Tweed ACCA

# ASSIGNMENT: HILLVIEW LEISURE – DEALING WITH CAPITAL TRANSACTIONS

**4**

## PERFORMANCE CRITERIA COVERED

The following performance criteria are covered by this assignment:

**Element 4.1 Maintain records relating to capital acquisition and disposal**

i    Relevant details relating to capital expenditure are correctly entered in the  appropriate records.

ii    The organisation's records agree with the physical presence of capital items.

iii    All acquisition and disposal costs and revenues are correctly identified and recorded in the appropriate records.

iv    Depreciation charges and other necessary entries and adjustments are correctly calculated and recorded in the appropriate records.

vi    Profit and loss on disposal is correctly calculated and recorded in the appropriate  records.

vii    The organisation's policies and procedures relating to the maintenance of capital records are adhered to.

ix    When possible, suggestions for improvements in the way the organisation maintains its capital records are made to the appropriate person.

## THE SITUATION

Hillview Leisure is a company in the leisure and entertainment business. It hires out anything from bouncy castles to sophisticated stage and lighting equipment to local businesses and also to the general public. All customers are expected to pay a 25% non-refundable deposit for any hire, and the balance is then due on completion.

You are employed by Hillview Leisure as the Assistant Group Accountant; the date is Monday 10 January 1999. You have been asked to complete a number of tasks so that the latest set of financial accounts can be completed.

You have been given details from the previous year's fixed asset registers for assets in ownership up until 31 December 1997. You  have also been given a number of figures and balances brought forward.

It is company policy to charge a full year's depreciation in the year of acquisition irrespective of the date of purchase and no depreciation is charged in the year of sale. All depreciation charges are rounded *up* to the nearest whole pound.  You are in all cases to assume a nil residual value.

---

**MOTOR VEHICLES**

| Date of Acquisition | Vehicle Ref. No | Description | Depreciation Rate % | Actual Cost £ | Accumulated Depreciation b/f £ |
|---|---|---|---|---|---|
| 27.05.95 | MV1 | Mercedes Van | 25% SLM | 35,000 | (26,250) |
| 14.08.96 | DM1 | Daimler Lorry | 25% SLM | 42,000 | (21,000) |
| 23.09.96 | DP2 | Datsun Pick-up | 25% SLM | 8,000 | (4,000) |
| 08.11.97 | MV2 | Mercedes Van | 25% SLM | 48,000 | (12,000) |
| 21.12.97 | TR1 | Daewoo Trailer | 25% SLM | 3,000 | (750) |

**LEISURE  EQUIPMENT**

| Date of Acquisition | Vehicle Ref. No | Description | Depreciation Rate % | Actual Cost £ | Accumulated Depreciation b/f £ |
|---|---|---|---|---|---|
| 23.03.95 | BC1 | Monkey Castle | 20% RBM | 5,000 | (2,440) |
| 23.03.95 | BC2 | Elephant Castle | 20% RBM | 8,000 | (3,904) |
| 02.06.96 | PS1 | Portable Stage | 20% RBM | 22,000 | (7,920) |
| 02.06.96 | SL1 | Stage Lighting | 20% RBM | 15,000 | (5,400) |
| 02.06.96 | GN1 | Generator | 20% RBM | 6,000 | (2,160) |
| 11.11.97 | BC3 | Giraffe Castle | 20% RBM | 7,500 | (1,500) |
| 11.11.97 | BC4 | Lion King Castle | 20% RBM | 6,500 | (1,300) |
| 28.12.97 | SL2 | Stage Lighting | 20% RBM | 20,500 | (4,100) |
| 28.12.97 | GN2 | Generator | 20% RBM | 8,500 | (1,700) |

**Note**   SLM  = The straight line method based on cost.

RBM  = The reduced balance method based on the net book value brought forward.

For the year ending 31 December 1998 the following Capital Expenditure was incurred (see the invoices illustrated on pages 101 t0 104)

---

**MOTOR VEHICLES**

| Date of Acquisition | Reference Number | Description | Actual Cost £ | Payment Terms | Depreciation Rate % |
|---|---|---|---|---|---|
| 13.03.98 | LD1 | Leyland DAF Van | 27,000 | HP* | 25% SLM |
| 14.09.98 | DP3 | Datsun Pick Up | 12,000 | Cheque + Part Exchange | 25% SLM |

*HP = Hire Purchase agreement

**LEISURE EQUIPMENT**

| Date of Acquisition | Reference Number | Description | Actual Cost £ | Payment Terms | Depreciation Rate % |
|---|---|---|---|---|---|
| 21.01.98 | MQ1 | Grand Marquee | 16,600 | IFC§ | 20% RBM |
| 24.04.98 | PS2 | Portable Stage | 19,900 | Cheque | 20% RBM |

§IFC = Interest Free Credit  (repaid by 24 monthly instalments)

---

**FURTHER INFORMATION AND GUIDANCE**

- When the new Datsun Pick-up (DP3) was purchased for £12,000, the other Datsun (DP2) was part exchanged at an agreed price of £4,750.

- During the year the Elephant Castle (BC2) was involved in an accident, when at a School fete some youths entered the bouncy castle with their shoes on and it was extensively ripped. However the castle was covered by insurance, and on 30 June 1998 the insurance company agreed to pay £3,500 by way of compensation.

# SALES INVOICE

## BNS Motors

24 The Bridle, Welland, Worcs WR7 4ER
Tel 01905 765365 Fax 01905 7659507
VAT Reg GB 0745 4172 20

invoice to

| Hillview Leisure Ltd |
| 24 Cross Keys Road |
| Malvern |
| Worcs |
| WR14 4PP |

| invoice no | BNS 99006 |
| account | H006 |
| your reference | DP3/(DP2) |
| date/tax point | 14 09 98 |

deliver to

as above

| details | quantity | price | amount (excl VAT) | VAT rate % | VAT amount £ |
|---|---|---|---|---|---|
| Datsun Pick Up | 1 | 12000.00 | 12000.00 | 17.5 | 2100.00 |
| less part-exchange | | | | | |
| Datsun Pick Up | 1 | (4750.00) | (4750.00) | 17.5 | 831.00 |

| Total (excl VAT) | 7250.00 |
|---|---|
| **VAT** | 1269.00 |
| **TOTAL** | 8519.00 |

# SALES INVOICE

## Black & Yellow Garage

Hallow Road, Hallow, Worcs WR5 4BB
Tel 01905 640365  Fax 01905 6409507
VAT Reg GB 0777 4172 26

invoice to

| | |
|---|---|
| Hillview Leisure Ltd | |
| 24 Cross Keys Road | |
| Malvern | |
| Worcs | |
| WR14 4PP | |

invoice no          BY1266

account             HL101

your reference      LD1

date/tax point      13 03 98

deliver to

as above

| details | quantity | price | amount (excl VAT) | VAT rate % | VAT amount £ |
|---|---|---|---|---|---|
| Leyland DAF Van | 1 | 27000.00 | 27000.00 | 17.5 | 4725.00 |

| | |
|---|---|
| **Total (excl VAT)** | 27000.00 |
| **VAT** | 4725.00 |
| **TOTAL** | 31725.00 |

# SALES INVOICE

## Professional Leisure Design

The Old Smithy, Blacksmith Lane, Hemel Hempstead, WD40 6TH
Tel 01702 765365  Fax 01702 7659507  Email eric@profleis.u-net.com
VAT Reg GB 1243 465327

invoice to

Hillview Leisure Ltd
24 Cross Keys Road
Malvern
Worcs
WR14 4PP

| | |
|---|---|
| invoice no | A197602 |
| account | HL066 |
| your reference | MQ1 |
| date/tax point | 21 01 98 |

deliver to

as above

| details | quantity | price | amount (excl VAT) | VAT rate % | VAT amount £ |
|---|---|---|---|---|---|
| Grand Marquee | 1 | 16600.00 | 16600.00 | 17.5 | 2905.00 |

| | |
|---|---|
| **Total (excl VAT)** | 16600.00 |
| **VAT** | 2905.00 |
| **TOTAL** | 19505.00 |

# SALES INVOICE

## Professional Leisure Design

The Old Smithy, Blacksmith Lane, Hemel Hempstead, WD40 6TH
Tel 01702 765365  Fax 01702 7659507  Email eric@profleis.u-net.com
VAT Reg GB 1243 465327

invoice to

| | |
|---|---|
| Hillview Leisure Ltd | |
| 24 Cross Keys Road | |
| Malvern | |
| Worcs | |
| WR14 4PP | |

| | |
|---|---|
| invoice no | A266942 |
| account | HL066 |
| your reference | PS2 |
| date/tax point | 24 04 98 |

deliver to

as above

| details | quantity | price | amount (excl VAT) | VAT rate % | VAT amount £ |
|---|---|---|---|---|---|
| Portable Stage | 1 | 19900.00 | 19900.00 | 17.5 | 3483.00 |

| | |
|---|---|
| **Total (excl VAT)** | 19900.00 |
| **VAT** | 3483.00 |
| **TOTAL** | 23383.00 |

## TASKS

1    Draw up the Fixed Asset Registers for the year to 31 December 1998. You can use the pro-forma registers shown on pages 106 to 109.

2    Another of your accounting duties includes the year-end adjustments and the book-keeping for capital transactions. You have therofore been requested to update the nominal ledger accounts for the year, these include the following:

Motor Vehicles at Cost Account

Provision for depreciation (Motor Vehicles) Account

Motor Vehicles Disposals Account

Leisure  Equipment at Cost Account

Provision for Depreciation (Leisure Equipment)  Account

Leisure Equipment Disposals Account

You can use the nominal ledger provided on pages 110 to 111.

3    Complete the journal entries for the scrapping of the Elephant Castle (BC2) on 30 June 1998. You should also support your journal with a suitable narrative.

Use the journal paper provided on page 112.

4    Hillview Leisure have recently recruited a new Accounts trainee, Sarah Smith, to whom you will act as adviser in the first year of  her employment. At present she knows very little about depreciation. Draft a brief memorandum which:

•   highlights  what depreciation actually is

•   summarises the factors that make it necessary

You may wish to make some reference to FRS 15 – Tangible fixed assets.

Use the memorandum on page 113.

## CATEGORY OF ASSET: MOTOR VEHICLES

| Date of Acquisition | Description | Ref. no. | Depreciation method | Actual Cost £ | Accumulated Depreciation brought/fwd (£) |
|---|---|---|---|---|---|
| | | | | | |

**YEAR TO**     **31 DECEMBER 1998**

| Date of Disposal | Depreciation charge this year (£) | Accumulated Depreciation carried fwd (£) | NBV carried fwd £ | Sale proceeds £ | Profit/(Loss) on disposal £ |
|---|---|---|---|---|---|
| | | | | | |

## CATEGORY OF ASSET: LEISURE EQUIPMENT

| Date of Acquisition | Description | Ref. no. | Depreciation method | Actual Cost £ | Accumulated Depreciation brought/fwd (£) |
|---|---|---|---|---|---|
| | | | | | |

**YEAR TO**     **31 DECEMBER 1998**

| Date of Disposal | Depreciation charge this year (£) | Accumulated Depreciation carried fwd (£) | NBV carried fwd £ | Sale proceeds £ | Profit/(Loss) on disposal £ |
|---|---|---|---|---|---|
|  |  |  |  |  |  |

# NOMINAL LEDGER

Dr                       **MOTOR VEHICLES AT COST**                  Cr

| Date | Details | Amount | Date | Details | Amount |
|------|---------|--------|------|---------|--------|
|      |         | £      |      |         | £      |
|      |         |        |      |         |        |
|      |         |        |      |         |        |

Dr       **PROVISION FOR DEPRECIATION (MOTOR VEHICLES)**        Cr

| Date | Details | Amount | Date | Details | Amount |
|------|---------|--------|------|---------|--------|
|      |         | £      |      |         | £      |
|      |         |        |      |         |        |
|      |         |        |      |         |        |

Dr                **MOTOR VEHICLES DISPOSALS (DP2)**               Cr

| Date | Details | Amount | Date | Details | Amount |
|------|---------|--------|------|---------|--------|
|      |         | £      |      |         | £      |
|      |         |        |      |         |        |
|      |         |        |      |         |        |

Dr                                    **LEISURE EQUIPMENT AT COST**                                    Cr

| Date | Details | Amount | Date | Details | Amount |
|------|---------|--------|------|---------|--------|
|      |         | £      |      |         | £      |
|      |         |        |      |         |        |

Dr                          **PROVISION FOR DEPRECIATION (LEISURE EQUIPMENT)**                          Cr

| Date | Details | Amount | Date | Details | Amount |
|------|---------|--------|------|---------|--------|
|      |         | £      |      |         | £      |
|      |         |        |      |         |        |

Dr                              **LEISURE EQUIPMENT DISPOSALS (BC2)**                              Cr

| Date | Details | Amount | Date | Details | Amount |
|------|---------|--------|------|---------|--------|
|      |         | £      |      |         | £      |
|      |         |        |      |         |        |

# JOURNAL

| Date | Details | Dr £ | Cr £ |
|------|---------|------|------|
|      |         |      |      |
|      |         |      |      |
|      |         |      |      |
|      |         |      |      |
|      |         |      |      |

# MEMORANDUM

**To:**

**From:**

**Subject:**                                    **Date:**

# ASSIGNMENT: MARSTON & BANKS – MANUFACTURING ACCOUNTS & PARTNERSHIPS

5

## PERFORMANCE CRITERIA COVERED

The following performance criteria are covered by this assignment.

### Element 4.2  Record income and expenditure

i    All income and expenditure is correctly identified and recorded in the appropriate records.

ii   Relevant accrued or prepaid income and expenditure is correctly identified and adjustments are made.

iii  The organisation's policies, regulations, procedures and timescales in relation to recording income and expenditure are observed.

### Element 4.3  Collect and collate information for the preparation of final accounts

i    Relevant accounts and reconciliations are correctly prepared to allow the preparation of final accounts.

ii   All relevant information is correctly identified and recorded.

iii  Investigations into business transactions are conducted with tact and courtesy.

iv  The organisation's policies, regulations, procedures and timescales relating to preparing final accounts are observed.

v   Discrepancies and unusual features  are identified and either resolved or referred to the appropriate person.

## SECTION 1 - THE SITUATION

Pete Marston and Tony Banks own and run a manufacturing company, buying in various cotton-based materials and converting them into designer fabrics, suitable for use as curtains and furniture covers.

Marston and Banks own large premises in the town of Cheltenham and they distribute their designs nationwide, either directly to chain stores or through agents.

You work for the company as part of the finance team. Your official title is Assistant Accountant and your responsibilities include year-end accounts which are then passed on to the Financial Controller, Kim West.

Today is 14 February 1999. You are required to produce the draft accounts for the year to 31 January 1999. You have been supplied with the following list of balances:

| | £ |
|---|---|
| Sales of finished goods | 857,500 |
| Advertising expenses | 15,760 |
| Delivery costs and motor expenses | 22,840 |
| Heat and light    Factory | 7,230 |
| Heat and light -  Office | 4,910 |
| Manufacturing wages | 65,980 |
| Telephone - Factory | 3,890 |
| Telephone - Office | 8,110 |
| Factory Managers salary | 25,000 |
| Repairs to Factory machinery | 3,880 |
| Repairs to Factory buildings | 1,230 |
| Administrative expenses - Office | 6,840 |
| General expenses - Factory | 8,290 |
| Manufacturing licence costs | 7,550 |
| Sales commission paid to agents | 37,520 |
| Bank charges and Interest | 5,890 |
| Purchase of fabric materials | 279,050 |
| Factory Machinery at cost | 500,000 |
| Provision for Depreciation - Factory Machinery as at 01.02.98 | 200,000 |
| Office salaries | 36,870 |
| Repairs to Office equipment | 4,440 |
| Factory cleaning and maintenance | 10,250 |
| Office cleaning and maintenance | 6,790 |
| Business rates - Factory | 4,000 |
| Business rates - Office | 6,000 |
| Buildings and Premises at cost | 3,000,000 |
| Provision for Depreciation- Buildings as at 01.02.98 | 200,000 |
| Opening Stocks as at 01 February 1998 | |
|     Fabric materials | 65,990 |
|     Work in progress | 14,320 |
|     Finished goods | 89,770 |
| Office Equipment at cost | 100,000 |
| Provision for Depreciation - Office equipment as at 01.02.98 | 40,000 |
| Motor Vehicles at cost | 96,000 |
| Provision for Depreciation - Motor vehicles as at 01.02.98 | 48,000 |

**ADDITIONAL INFORMATION**

The following information has been given relating to closing stock valuations and depreciation policy:

| Closing Stocks as at 31 January 1999 | £ |
|---|---|
| Fabric materials | 59,010 |
| Work in progress | 12,660 |
| Finished Goods | 69,690 |

Marston and Banks use the straight line depreciation method based on cost for all their assets, using the following rates:

| | |
|---|---|
| Factory Machinery | 10% |
| Office equipment | 20% |
| Buildings | 5% |
| Motor vehicles | 25% |

It is important to note that land and buildings at cost amount to £3,000,000, of which £2,000,000 is the valuation placed upon the land and this is *not* depreciated. This year's charge for depreciation on the buildings should be apportioned as an expense based on 40% to the factory and 60% to the office.

## SECTION 1 TASKS

**1.1**    Prepare a Manufacturing, Trading and Profit and Loss account for the year ended 31 January 1999, showing clearly the following:

- Prime cost

- Total cost of manufacture

- Gross profit

- Net profit

You may use the format shown on the next two pages.

**1.2**    Tony Banks has recently returned from a local Chamber of Commerce conference where the main theme for the day was the creation of cost centres for manufacturers. This even included the factory where a system of transfer pricing was discussed together with the 'provision for unrealised profit.'

Tony was unable to digest all the information straightaway and he has now asked you to summarise these key points on paper for you.

You may use the memorandum form shown on page 119.

## MARSTON & BANKS

## MANUFACTURING ACCOUNT FOR THE YEAR TO 31 JANUARY 1999

| | £ | £ |
|---|---|---|

PRIME COST

*Add* Factory Overheads:

Total Factory Cost

*Add* opening stock of work-in-progress

*Less* closing stock of work-in-progess

TOTAL COST OF MANUFACTURE

**MARSTON & BANKS**

**TRADING & PROFIT & LOSS ACCOUNT FOR THE YEAR TO 31 JANUARY 1999**

£   £

GROSS PROFIT

*Less:*

NET PROFIT

# MEMORANDUM

**To:**

**From:**

**Subject:**                                      **Date:**

## SECTION 2 – THE SITUATION

Marston and Banks own a second business, a retail shop which sells household goods. It is also used as a discount shop for their fabric designs which prove less popular with the public and therefore difficult to sell.

Pete Marston takes a greater interest in the shop than Tony Banks, and as a consequence they share the profits and losses on a 60% (Marston) and 40% (Banks) basis. Their latest trial balance after the completion of their trading profit and loss account (for the year to 31 December 1998) is as follows:

|  | Dr | Cr |
| --- | --- | --- |
|  | £ | £ |
| Buildings at cost | 120,000 |  |
| Provision for depreciation - Buildings |  | 24,000 |
| Fixtures and Fittings at cost | 30,000 |  |
| Provision for depreciation - Fixtures and Fittings |  | 13,500 |
| Delivery Van at cost | 28,000 |  |
| Provision for depreciation - Delivery Van |  | 7,000 |
| Creditors |  | 18,250 |
| Cash In Hand | 400 |  |
| Cash at Bank | 3,650 |  |
| Stock at 31.12.98 | 19,750 |  |
| Bank loan Account |  | 33,500 |
| Capital accounts:  Marston |  | 50,000 |
| Banks |  | 31,000 |
| Current Accounts:  Marston | 150 |  |
| Banks |  | 12,300 |
| Drawings:  Marston | 22,500 |  |
| Banks | 16,250 |  |
| Net profit for the year |  | 51,150 |
|  | 240,700 | 240,700 |

## SECTION 2 TASKS

**2.1**  Prepare the updated current accounts for both partners using the agreed profit sharing ratios. Use the format set out on the next page.

**2.2**  Prepare the partnership balance sheet as at 31 December 1998. Use the format on page 122.

## MARSTON & BANKS CURRENT ACCOUNTS

| | Marston £ | Banks £ | | Marston £ | Banks £ |
|---|---|---|---|---|---|
| | | | | | |

**MARSTON & BANKS**
**BALANCE SHEET AS AT 31 DECEMBER 1998**

|  | £ | £ | £ |
|---|---|---|---|
| FIXED ASSETS |  |  |  |
| CURRENT ASSETS |  |  |  |
| CURRENT LIABILITIES |  |  |  |
| NET CURRENT ASSETS |  |  |  |
| LONG TERM LIABILITIES |  |  |  |
| REPRESENTED BY:<br>CAPITAL ACCOUNTS |  |  |  |
| CURRENT ACCOUNTS |  |  |  |

# ASSIGNMENT: BON VOYAGE LIMITED – BANK RECONCILIATIONS AND CONTROL ACCOUNTS

**6**

## PERFORMANCE CRITERIA COVERED

The following performance criteria are covered by this assignment.

### Element 4.2  Record income and expenditure

i    All income and expenditure is correctly identified and recorded in the appropriate records.

ii   Relevant accrued or prepaid income and expenditure is correctly identified and adjustments are made.

iii  The organisation's policies, regulations, procedures and timescales in relation to recording income and expenditure are observed.

iv   Incomplete data is identified and either resolved or referred to the appropriate person.

## THE SITUATION

You work as an Accounts Assistant with the firm Bon Voyage Ltd and have responsibilities for the book-keeping and various month-end procedures. These include a series of controls which are performed as part of the firm's internal control procedure. Part of this policy includes the reconciliation of the cash book to the bank statements, and the reconciliation of the purchase ledger control account to the individual supplier account balances.

The tasks in this assignment are divided into two sections.

## SECTION 1 – DATA

It is the first week of January 1999. The summarised cash book for the month of December 1998 is shown below.

| Cash Book | | | | | Page 112 |
|---|---|---|---|---|---|
| 1998 | | £ | 1998 | | £ |
| Dec 01 | Sundry credit - sales | 22,567 | Dec 01 | Balance b/d | 11,332 |
| Dec 03 | Sundry credit - sales | 19,554 | Dec 03 | Insurance | 12,878 |
| Dec 05 | Sundry credit - sales | 24,770 | Dec 08 | Rich Ltd - Supplier | 33,898 |
| Dec 10 | Sundry credit - sales | 17,666 | Dec 09 | Motor Car | 17,560 |
| Dec 13 | Sundry credit - sales | 22,010 | Dec 12 | Poor Ltd - Supplier | 24,275 |
| Dec 16 | Sundry credit - sales | 15,345 | Dec 15 | Ginola - Supplier | 16,939 |
| Dec 20 | Sundry credit - sales | 18,444 | Dec 22 | Donation | 10,000 |
| Dec 23 | Sundry credit - sales | 29,233 | Dec 24 | Salaries | 54,887 |
| Dec 28 | Sundry credit - sales | 24,666 | Dec 29 | Court Ltd - Supplier | 8,777 |
| Dec 31 | Sundry credit - sales | 39,556 | Dec 30 | Sharp Ltd - Supplier | 16,882 |
| Dec 31 | Balance c/d | 3,067 | Dec 31 | Staff bonuses | 29,450 |
| | | 233,811 | | | 233,811 |
| | | | 1999 | | |
| | | | Jan 01 | Balance b/d | 3,067 |

Just arrived in the post is the bank statement for December 1998:

---

## Centro Bank PLC ───────────────────────────

**Branch**
119 Hallow Road, Suckley WR6 2RN

**Account**   Bon Voyage Limited          **Account No.**   12036754          **Statement No.**   135

| 1998 | | Dr | Cr | Balance | |
|---|---|---|---|---|---|
| | | £ | £ | £ | |
| Dec 01 | Balance b/f | | | 18,667 | O/D |
| Dec 02 | Sundry credit | | 44,583 | 25,916 | |
| Dec 03 | Cheque 313 | 12,910 | | 13,006 | |
| Dec 04 | Cheque 314 | 12,878 | | 128 | |
| Dec 05 | Sundry credit | | 22,567 | 22,695 | |
| Dec 07 | Cheque 311 | 11,416 | | 11,279 | |
| Dec 08 | Sundry credit | | 19,554 | 30,833 | |
| Dec 11 | Bank charges | 400 | | | |
| Dec 11 | Bank Interest | 1,253 | | 29,180 | |
| Dec 12 | Sundry credit | | 24,770 | 53,950 | |
| Dec 13 | Cheque 315 | 33,898 | | 20,052 | |
| Dec 15 | Cheque 312 | 12,922 | | 7,130 | |
| Dec 16 | Transfer G/A | 9,190 | | 2,060 | O/D |
| Dec 17 | Sundry Credit | | 17,666 | 15,606 | |
| Dec 18 | UBR Rates -standing order | 4,250 | | 11,356 | |
| Dec 19 | Sundry credit | | 22,010 | 33,366 | |
| Dec 20 | Cheque 316 | 17,560 | | 15,806 | |
| Dec 21 | Sundry credit | | 15,345 | 31,151 | |
| Dec 23 | Cheque 317 | 24,275 | | 6,876 | |
| Dec 26 | Cheque 318 | 16,939 | | 10,063 | O/D |
| Dec 28 | Cheque 320 | 54,887 | | 64,950 | O/D |
| Dec 29 | Sundry credit | | 18,444 | 46,506 | O/D |
| Dec 31 | Sundry credit | | 29,233 | 17,273 | O/D |

O/D  Denotes overdrawn balance

## SECTION 1 – TASKS

**1.1** Draw up an opening bank reconciliation as at 1st January 1999. Use the pro-forma shown below.

**1.2** Write up the cash book to date, making any adjustments to the closing balance that you feel are necessary. Use the cash book on page 127.

**1.3** Complete the bank reconciliation statement for 31 January 1999. Use the form shown on page 127.

**1.4** Write a memorandum to Jim Basinger, accounts trainee, listing the reasons why bank reconciliations should be carried out on a monthly basis. Use the form on page 128. Use your own name and a date in the first week of January 1999.

---

**BANK RECONCILIATION STATEMENT AS AT** ........................................................................................

Balance as per bank statement, date .................................................................................

less unpresented lodgements

add unrepresented cheques

BALANCE PER CASH BOOK

## Cash Book

Page 113

| 1998 | | £ | 1998 | | £ |
|------|--|---|------|--|---|
| | | | | | |
| | | | | | |
| | | | | | |
| | | | | | |
| | | | | | |

---

**BANK RECONCILIATION STATEMENT AS AT** ..........................................................

Balance as per bank statement, date ...................................................................

less unpresented lodgements

add unrepresented cheques

BALANCE PER CASH BOOK

# MEMORANDUM

**To:**

**From:**

**Subject:**                                              **Date:**

## SECTION 2 – DATA

One of your duties is to balance off the purchase ledger control account each month against the individual supplier account balances contained in the creditors ledger. To assist with the book-keeping, Bon Voyage Ltd incorporates the control account as part of the double-entry procedure and then checks it against the total of the creditors' accounts, which are maintained as memorandum accounts, and are therefore not part of the double-entry system.

The following purchase ledger control account has been prepared by Jim Basinger, the trainee, but unfortunately it does not agree to the individual list of supplier balances contained in the creditors ledger.

| Purchase Ledger Control Account | | | |
|---|---|---|---|
| | £ | | £ |
| Paid to suppliers | 867,990 | Balance b/d | 104,871 |
| Discount received | 25,660 | Credit purchases | 1,056,890 |
| Returns outwards | 33,250 | | |
| Sales ledger contra | 75,890 | | |
| Balance c/d | 158,971 | | |
| | 1,161,761 | | 1,161,761 |
| | | Balance b/d | 158,971 |

The total of the individual balances in the Creditors ledger has been totalled at £209,521 (net) but an investigation into the book-keeping revealed the following:

1.  A debit balance of £14,780 on an individual supplier account within the creditors ledger was included in the calculation of the total balances as though it was a credit balance.

2.  One of the pages in the Purchase day book was totalled incorrectly. The total was £18,000 less than the correct sum of the individual entries.

3.  A credit note received from a supplier for £6,500 had been entered into the returns outwards day book as £5,600.

4.  No entries had been made in the individual supplier accounts to record some of the sales ledger account contras. The transactions omitted totalled £12,080.

5.  An individual supplier account High Density Ltd has been extracted as a credit balance of £23,230 instead of the correct credit balance of £32,320.

## SECTION 2 – TASKS

**2.1** Make any entries that you consider are necessary to the Purchase ledger control account and to the individual list of creditor balances. At the end of your adjustments, the two closing balances should reconcile.

Use the control account layout below and the supplier balance listing form shown on the next page.

**2.2** Control accounts appear in most large businesses as part of the book-keeping process. One of the main reasons for this is that such accounts act as 'an aid to management.' Briefly explain to Jim Basinger, the accounts trainee, in what areas control accounts assist the management function within a business. Use the memorandum shown on page 132.

| PURCHASE LEDGER CONTROL ACCOUNT | |
|---|---|
| | £ |
| | Balance b/d 158,971 |

| SUPPLIER BALANCE LISTING | |
|---|---|
| | £ |
| Balance b/d | 209,521 |

# MEMORANDUM

**To:**

**From:**

**Subject:**                                           **Date:**

# Simulation 1
## Branson & Company

reproduced by kind permission of AAT

suggested time limit 4 hours

### SCENARIO

This simulation is based on a manufacturing company which produces a product known as a 'mendip'. The tasks include:

- recording the purchase and disposal of a company car
- updating the fixed assets register
- postings to the nominal ledger
- preparation of a bank reconciliaton statement
- correction of errors and making of adjustments
- stock valuation
- preparation of the extended trial balance

### NVQ UNIT 4 – ELEMENTS COVERED

1   maintain records relating to capital acquisition and disposal
2   record income and expenditure
3   collect and collate information for the preparation of final accounts
4   prepare the extended trial balance

# SIMULATION
# BRANSON & COMPANY

## THE SITUATION

Your name is Val Denning and you are an accounts assistant working for Branson & Co, a partnership business owned by two partners called Amy Brandreth and Sanjay Sondin. You report to the firm's Accountant, Jenny Holden.

Branson is a manufacturing business, purchasing raw materials and producing a finished product called a mendip. The manufacturing process is very simple, involving the assembly of just two bought-in parts and a small amount of finishing work. The firm's stocks consist of raw materials (the bought-in parts) and finished mendips; work in progress is negligible in value at any time.

This simulation relates to Branson's accounting year ended 31 March 1998. Today's date is 20 April 1998.

### books and records

Branson maintains a full system of ledger accounts in manual format. Money coming in and going out is recorded in a manual cash book which serves both as a book of prime entry and as a ledger account.

Branson also maintains a manual fixed assets register. This includes details of capital expenditure (but not revenue expenditure) incurred in acquiring or enhancing fixed assets, as well as details of depreciation and disposals.

### accounting policies and procedures

Branson is registered for VAT and all of its sales are standard-rated.

Branson classifies its fixed assets into three categories: company cars, plant and equipment, and other fixed assets. For each category the nominal (general) ledger includes accounts relating to cost, depreciation charge (ie the profit and loss expense), accumulated depreciation (ie the balance sheet provision), and disposals.

Company cars are depreciated at a rate of 45% per annum on the reducing balance. Plant and equipment and other fixed assets are depreciated at 25% per annum straight line, assuming nil residual value. In the year of an asset's acquisition a full year's depreciation is charged, regardless of the exact date of acquisition. In the year of an asset's disposal, no depreciation is charged. Company car running costs are recorded in the firm's accounts as an administration overhead. Branson is not able to recover input VAT on the purchase of company cars. Similarly, the firm is not required to account for output VAT when company cars are disposed of.

Authorisation for the acquisition and disposal of fixed assets, and for the method of finance derives from the partners and is communicated to you by means of a memo from the firm's Accountant at the beginning of each month in which an acquisition or disposal is planned. In the month of March 1998 one acquisition and one disposal took place; these are referred to in the memo on page 137.

### the simulation

In this simulation you will be required to perform a number of tasks leading up to the preparation of an extended trial balance for the year ended 31 March 1998.

## SUMMARY OF TASKS TO BE COMPLETED

1   Refer to the memo on page 137 and the supplier's invoice on page 138. This refers to the purchase of a new company car and the trade-in of an existing company car. You are required to record the acquisition and the trade-in in the fixed assets register (see page 141) and in the nominal ledger (which starts on page 142). You are reminded that Branson is not able to recover VAT on the acquisition of company cars.

2   By reference to the fixed assets register, you are required to calculate the depreciation for the year on each of the company cars and also on each item of plant and equipment. You should record the relevant amounts in the fixed assets register and in the nominal (general) ledger. You should also calculate the depreciation for the year on 'other fixed assets' and record the relevant amount in the nominal ledger.

3   A member of staff has listed the company cars actually present on Branson's premises at the close of business on 31 March 1998. His list is on page 151. You are required to compare this list with the details recorded in the fixed assets register and to describe any discrepancies in a memo to the firm's Accountant. Use the memo form on page 152.

4   The nominal (general) ledger already includes sales and purchases transactions up to 28 February 1998. The sales and purchases day books have been totalled for March 1998 and the totals are displayed on page 151. You are required to post these totals to the nominal (general) ledger. Note that the invoice from Task 1 was not included in the March totals because it was not received until April.

5   Refer to the business bank statement and the business cash book on pages 153 and 154. You are required to perform a bank reconciliation as at 31 March 1998. Set out your bank reconciliation on page 155.

6   You are required to post from the business cash book to the nominal (general) ledger for the month of March 1998.

7   You are required to bring down a balance as at 1 April 1998 on each account in the nominal ledger (pages 142 to 151) and to enter the balances in the first two columns of the trial balance (page156). The totals of the two columns will not be equal. You should establish why, and make the appropriate addition to the trial balance.

8   The debit entry in the suspense account (£750) represents a cheque made out on the business bank account earlier in the year. The payee is not known to you as a supplier or employee of Branson. You are required to describe how you would ascertain the nature of this payment so that you can account for it correctly. Set out your answer on page 158.

   (Note: once you have completed this task you should ask your assessor to explain what the payment represents. You will need this information to complete Task 9.)

9   The credit entry on the suspense account is the proceeds on disposal of a fixed asset included in the category 'other fixed assets'. No other entries have been made in the nominal ledger in respect of this disposal. The asset originally cost £2,317.69, and its accumulated depreciation at 31 March 1997 was £946.23. You are required to draft journal entries dated 31 March 1998, to clear the

balance on the suspense account. Set out your entries, with full narrative, on page 158. (Note: you are not required to adjust your answer to Task 2 in the light of this transaction.)

10   Details of Branson's closing stocks are given on page 159. You are required to calculate the value of the closing stock of raw materials and finished goods at 31 March 1998 for inclusion in the trial balance. Use page 160 for your answer. Note that to calculate the value of finished goods stock you will need to prepare a manufacturing account for the year ended 31 March 1998.

11   On the trial balance you are required to make appropriate adjustments in respect of the following matters:

- The journal entries prepared in Task 9

- Closing stock calculated in Task 10

- Accruals and prepayments. For details of these see page 159.

12   You are required to extend the trial balance (page 157). This includes totalling all columns of the trial balance and making entries to record the net profit or loss for the year ended 31 March 1998.

# MEMORANDUM

**To:**        Val Denning

**From:**      Jenny Holden

**Subject:**   Fixed asset acquisitions/disposals in March 1998

**Date:**      2 March 1998


Only one fixed asset acquisition is planned for the month of March.  Our salesman, Andy Noble, will trade in his old car (registration M104 PTY) and purchase a new one.  The new one will be financed partly by the trade-in value (agreed at £1,850), and partly by cash.

## SALES INVOICE

# HYLEX MOTORS

45 Extines Road, Blankton
Telephone: 01489 22514  Fax: 01489 56178
VAT registration: GB 318 1627 66

Date/tax point 27 March 1998

Invoice no 42176

Invoice to:

Branson & Co
Unit 6 Chalmers Industrial Estate
Blankton
BT3 4NY

Registration: R261 GHT Registration date: 27/3/98 Stock number: Q4510
Chassis no: TWQQAW 66780 Engine no: ER43218 Sales person: M Easton

|  | £ |
|---|---|
| Ford Mondeo (list price) | 10,900.00 |
| VAT at 17.5% | 1,907.50 |
|  | 12,807.50 |
| Vehicle excise duty  (12 months) | 140.00 |
| Total due | 12,947.50 |
| Less: part-exchange (M104 OTY) | 1,850.00 |
| Balance to pay | 11,097.50 |

Terms: net, 30 days

# EXTRACTS FROM FIXED ASSETS REGISTER

| Description/serial no | Location | Date acquired | Original cost £ | Enhance-ments £ | Total £ | Deprecia-tion £ | NBV £ | Funding method | Disposal proceeds £ | Disposal date |
|---|---|---|---|---|---|---|---|---|---|---|
| **Plant and equipment** | | | | | | | | | | |
| Milling machine 45217809 | Factory | 20/6/94 | 3,456.08 | | 3,456.08 | | | Cash | | |
| Year ended 31/3/95 | | | | | | 864.02 | 2,592.06 | | | |
| Year ended 31/3/96 | | | | | | 864.02 | 1,728.04 | | | |
| Year ended 31/3/97 | | | | | | 864.02 | 864.02 | | | |
| Lathe 299088071 | Factory | 12/6/95 | 4,008.24 | | 4,008.24 | | | Cash | | |
| Year ended 31/3/96 | | | | | | 1,002.06 | 3,006.18 | | | |
| Year ended 31/3/97 | | | | | | 1,002.06 | 2,004.12 | | | |
| Drill assembly 51123412 | Factory | 12/2/96 | 582.44 | | 582.44 | | | Cash | | |
| Year ended 31/3/96 | | | | | | 145.61 | 436.83 | | | |
| Year ended 31/3/97 | | | | | | 145.61 | 291.22 | | | |
| Punch drive 91775321 | Factory | 12/2/96 | 1,266.00 | | 1,266.00 | | | Cash plus trade-in | | |
| Year ended 31/3/96 | | | | | | 316.50 | 949.50 | | | |
| Year ended 31/3/97 | | | | | | 316.50 | 633.00 | | | |
| Winding gear 53098871 | Factory | 13/3/96 | 1,082.68 | | 1,082.68 | | | Cash | | |
| Year ended 31/3/96 | | | | | | 270.67 | 812.01 | | | |
| Year ended 31/3/97 | | | | 34.79 | 1,153.80 | 384.60 | 769.20 | | | |

# EXTRACTS FROM FIXED ASSETS REGISTER

**needed for Tasks 1 & 2**

| Description/serial no | Location | Date acquired | Original cost £ | Enhancements £ | Total £ | Depreciation £ | NBV £ | Funding method | Disposal proceeds £ | Disposal date |
|---|---|---|---|---|---|---|---|---|---|---|
| Tender press 44231809 | Factory | 8/8/96 | 4,256.04 | | 4,256.04 | | | Cash | | |
| Year ended 31/3/97 | | | | | | 1,064.01 | 3,192.03 | | | |

# EXTRACTS FROM FIXED ASSETS REGISTER

needed for Tasks 1 & 2

| Description/serial no | Location | Date acquired | Original cost £ | Enhance-ments £ | Total £ | Deprecia-tion £ | NBV £ | Funding method | Disposal proceeds £ | Disposal date |
|---|---|---|---|---|---|---|---|---|---|---|
| **Company cars** | | | | | | | | | | |
| M412 RTW | Yard | 25/8/94 | 8,923.71 | | 8,923.71 | | | Lease | | |
| Year ended 31/3/95 | | | | | | 4,015.67 | 4,908.04 | | | |
| Year ended 31/3/96 | | | | | | 2,208.62 | 2,699.42 | | | |
| Year ended 31/3/97 | | | | | | 1,214.74 | 1,484.68 | | | |
| | | | | | | | | | | |
| M104 PTY | Yard | 15/3/95 | 8,643.00 | | 8,643.00 | | | Cash | | |
| Year ended 31/3/95 | | | | | | 3,889.35 | 4,753.65 | | | |
| Year ended 31/3/96 | | | | | | 2,139.14 | 2,614.51 | | | |
| Year ended 31/3/97 | | | | | | 1,176.53 | 1,437.98 | | | |
| | | | | | | | | | | |
| N33 FGY | Yard | 18/9/95 | 10,065.34 | | 10,065.34 | | | Cash plus trade-in | | |
| Year ended 31/3/96 | | | | | | 4,529.40 | 5,535.94 | | | |
| Year ended 31/3/97 | | | | | | 2,491.17 | 3,044.77 | | | |
| | | | | | | | | | | |
| P321 HDR | Yard | 13/12/96 | 9,460.26 | | 9,460.26 | | | Cash | | |
| Year ended 31/3/97 | | | | | | 4,257.12 | 5,203.14 | | | |

# nominal ledger (extract)

needed for Tasks 1,2,4,6,7

**Account**  Administration overheads
Debit                                                                      Credit

| Date 1998 | Details | Amount £ | Date 1998 | Details | Amount £ |
|---|---|---|---|---|---|
| 1-Mar | Balance b/f | 15,071.23 | | | |

**Account**  Brandreth capital account
Debit                                                                      Credit

| Date 1998 | Details | Amount £ | Date 1998 | Details | Amount £ |
|---|---|---|---|---|---|
| | | | 1-Mar | Balance b/f | 17,063.24 |

**Account**  Brandreth current account
Debit                                                                      Credit

| Date 1998 | Details | Amount £ | Date 1998 | Details | Amount £ |
|---|---|---|---|---|---|
| 1-Mar | Balance b/f | 11,056.73 | | | |

## nominal ledger (extract)

**Account** Company cars: cost

| Date 1998 | Details | Amount £ | Date 1998 | Details | Amount £ |
|---|---|---|---|---|---|
| 1-Mar | Balance b/f | 37,092.31 | | | |

Debit — Credit

**Account** Company cars: depreciation charge

| Date 1998 | Details | Amount £ | Date 1998 | Details | Amount £ |
|---|---|---|---|---|---|
| | | | | | |

Debit — Credit

**Account** Company cars: accumulated depreciation

| Date 1997 | Details | Amount £ | Date 1997 | Details | Amount £ |
|---|---|---|---|---|---|
| | | | 1-Apr | Balance b/f | 25,921.74 |

Debit — Credit

## nominal ledger (extract)

**Account** Company cars: disposals
Debit                                                    Credit

| Date 1998 | Details | Amount £ | Date 1998 | Details | Amount £ |
|---|---|---|---|---|---|
|  |  |  |  |  |  |

**Account** Direct labour costs
Debit                                                    Credit

| Date 1998 | Details | Amount £ | Date 1998 | Details | Amount £ |
|---|---|---|---|---|---|
| 1-Mar | Balance b/f | 60,012.64 |  |  |  |

**Account** Factory overheads
Debit                                                    Credit

| Date 1998 | Details | Amount £ | Date 1998 | Details | Amount £ |
|---|---|---|---|---|---|
| 1-Mar | Balance b/f | 27,109.67 |  |  |  |

## nominal ledger (extract)

**Account** Other fixed assets: cost
Debit                                                    Credit

| Date 1998 | Details | Amount £ | Date 1998 | Details | Amount £ |
|---|---|---|---|---|---|
| 1-Mar | Balance b/f | 18,923.50 | | | |

**Account** Other fixed assets: depreciation charge
Dobit                                                    Credlt

| Date 1998 | Details | Amount £ | Date 1998 | Details | Amount £ |
|---|---|---|---|---|---|
| | | | | | |

**Account** Other fixed assets: accumulated depreciation
Debit                                                    Credit

| Date 1997 | Details | Amount £ | Date 1997 | Details | Amount £ |
|---|---|---|---|---|---|
| | | | 1-Apr | Balance b/f | 6,224.12 |

## nominal ledger (extract)

| **Account** Other fixed assets: disposals | | | | | |
| Debit | | | Credit | | |
| Date 1998 | Details | Amount £ | Date 1998 | Details | Amount £ |
|---|---|---|---|---|---|
| | | | | | |
| | | | | | |

| **Account** Plant and equipment: cost | | | | | |
| Debit | | | Credit | | |
| Date 1998 | Details | Amount £ | Date 1998 | Details | Amount £ |
|---|---|---|---|---|---|
| 1-Mar | Balance b/f | 14,993.27 | | | |
| | | | | | |

| **Account** Plant and equipment: depreciation charge | | | | | |
| Debit | | | Credit | | |
| Date 1998 | Details | Amount £ | Date 1998 | Details | Amount £ |
|---|---|---|---|---|---|
| | | | | | |
| | | | | | |

# nominal ledger (extract)

| Account Plant and equipment: accumulated depreciation | | | | | |
|---|---|---|---|---|---|
| Debit | | | Credit | | |
| Date 1997 | Details | Amount £ | Date 1997 | Details | Amount £ |
| | | | 1-Apr | Balance b/f | 7,239.68 |

| Account Plant and equipment: disposals | | | | | |
|---|---|---|---|---|---|
| Debit | | | Credit | | |
| Date 1998 | Details | Amount £ | Date 1998 | Details | Amount £ |
| | | | | | |

| Account Purchases | | | | | |
|---|---|---|---|---|---|
| Debit | | | Credit | | |
| Date 1998 | Details | Amount £ | Date 1998 | Details | Amount £ |
| 1-Mar | Balance b/f | 54,231.89 | | | |

## nominal ledger (extract)

**Account** Purchases ledger control
Debit                                            Credit

| Date 1998 | Details | Amount £ | Date 1998 | Details | Amount £ |
|---|---|---|---|---|---|
| | | | 1-Mar | Balance b/f | 18,457.20 |
| | | | | | |
| | | | | | |
| | | | | | |
| | | | | | |

**Account** Sales
Debit                                            Credit

| Date 1998 | Details | Amount £ | Date 1998 | Details | Amount £ |
|---|---|---|---|---|---|
| | | | 1-Mar | Balance b/f | 225,091.42 |
| | | | | | |
| | | | | | |
| | | | | | |
| | | | | | |

**Account** Sales ledger control
Debit                                            Credit

| Date 1998 | Details | Amount £ | Date 1998 | Details | Amount £ |
|---|---|---|---|---|---|
| 1-Mar | Balance b/f | 24,617.03 | | | |
| | | | | | |
| | | | | | |
| | | | | | |
| | | | | | |

# nominal ledger (extract)

| Account Selling and distribution overheads Debit | | | Credit | | |
|---|---|---|---|---|---|
| Date 1998 | Details | Amount £ | Date 1998 | Details | Amount £ |
| 1-Mar | Balance b/f | 14,303.12 | | | |

| Account Sondin capital account Debit | | | Credit | | |
|---|---|---|---|---|---|
| Date 1998 | Details | Amount £ | Date 1998 | Details | Amount £ |
| | | | 1-Mar | Balance b/f | 8,703.28 |

| Account Sondin current account Debit | | | Credit | | |
|---|---|---|---|---|---|
| Date 1998 | Details | Amount £ | Date 1998 | Details | Amount £ |
| 1-Mar | Balance b/f | 12,912.29 | | | |

## nominal ledger (extract)

**Account** Stock: raw materials
Debit                                                    Credit

| Date 1997 | Details | Amount £ | Date 1997 | Details | Amount £ |
|---|---|---|---|---|---|
| 1-Apr | Balance b/f | 6,294.33 | | | |

**Account** Stock: finished goods
Debit                                                    Credit

| Date 1997 | Details | Amount £ | Date 1997 | Details | Amount £ |
|---|---|---|---|---|---|
| 1-Apr | Balance b/f | 12,513.77 | | | |

**Account** Suspense
Debit                                                    Credit

| Date 1998 | Details | Amount £ | Date 1998 | Details | Amount £ |
|---|---|---|---|---|---|
| 26-Jan | Bank | 750.00 | 24-Feb | Bank | 1,124.55 |

## nominal ledger (extract)

| **Account** VAT | | | | | |
|---|---|---|---|---|---|
| Debit | | | Credit | | |
| Date 1998 | Details | Amount £ | Date 1998 | Details | Amount £ |
| | | | 1-Mar | Balance b/f | 5,091.27 |
| | | | | | |

---

**data for Task 3**

# COMPANY CARS ON THE PREMISES, 31 MARCH 1998

P321 HDR - in yard; N33 FGY - in yard; R261 GHT - in yard

---

**data for Task 4**

| Sales day book totals, March 1998 | £ |
|---|---|
| Total value of invoices | 36,514.59 |
| Sales value | 31,076.25 |
| VAT | 5,438.34 |

| Purchases day book totals, March 1998 | £ |
|---|---|
| Total value of invoices | 9,133.18 |
| Administration overheads | 991.24 |
| Factory overheads | 1,451.09 |
| Purchases | 4,871.22 |
| Selling and distribution overheads | 524.87 |
| VAT | 1,294.76 |

needed for Task 3

# MEMORANDUM

**To:**

**From:**

**Subject:**

**Date:**

# Northern Bank plc

26 High Street, Blankton BT1 6FG

Account: Branson & Co
Account no: 28771243

## STATEMENT

45—43—20

Statement no: 192

| Details | Payments £ | Receipts £ | Date | Balance £ |
|---|---|---|---|---|
| | | | 1998 | |
| Balance forward | | | 1–Mar | 1,912.90 |
| 19328 | 1,105.36 | | 3–Mar | 807.54 |
| CC | | 4,227.18 | 4–Mar | 5,034.72 |
| 19332 | 365.11 | | 10–Mar | 4,669.61 |
| CC | | 4,265.77 | 11–Mar | 8,935.38 |
| 19331 | 1,192.45 | | 12–Mar | 7,742.93 |
| 19333 | 2,651.08 | | 16–Mar | 5,091.85 |
| CC | | 5,931.20 | 18–Mar | 11,023.05 |
| 19335 | 299.52 | | 23–Mar | 10,723.53 |
| 19334 | 3,006.12 | | 24–Mar | 7,717.41 |
| CC | | 3,773.81 | 25–Mar | 11,491.22 |
| 19340 | 10,480.05 | | 30–Mar | 1,011.17 |
| 19336 | 2,561.29 | | 31–Mar | 1,550.12 O/D |

Key   S/O Standing order   DD Direct debit   CC Cash and/or cheques   CHGS Charges
BACS Bankers automated clearing services   O/D Overdrawn

**data for Task 5**

# CASHBOOK

CB122

| RECEIPTS | | | | | PAYMENTS | | | |
| Total £ | Sales ledger control £ | Other £ | Date 1998 | Details | Cheque no | Total £ | Purchases ledger control £ | Other £ |
|---|---|---|---|---|---|---|---|---|
| 5,034.72 | | | 1–Mar | Balance b/f | | | | |
| 4,265.77 | 4,265.77 | | 6–Mar | Cash and cheques banked | | | | |
| 5,931.20 | 5,931.20 | | 13–Mar | Cash and cheques banked | | | | |
| 3,773.81 | 3,773.81 | | 20–Mar | Cash and cheques banked | | | | |
| 6,071.88 | 6,071.88 | | 27–Mar | Cash and cheques banked | | | | |
| 5,512.67 | 5,512.67 | | 31–Mar | Cash and cheques banked | | | | |
| | | | 3–Mar | Hanway plc | 19331 | 1,192.45 | 1,192.45 | |
| | | | 5–Mar | Peters Limited | 19332 | 365.11 | 365.11 | |
| | | | 9–Mar | Wright & Parkin | 19333 | 2,651.08 | 2,651.08 | |
| | | | 16–Mar | Westcott Limited | 19334 | 3,006.12 | 3,006.12 | |
| | | | 17–Mar | Sidlow & Morris | 19335 | 299.52 | 299.52 | |
| | | | 24–Mar | Harper John & Co | 19336 | 2,561.29 | 2,561.29 | |
| | | | 24–Mar | Paul Darby plc | 19337 | 278.01 | 278.01 | |
| | | | 27–Mar | Brandreth: drawings | 19338 | 500.00 | | 500.00 |
| | | | 27–Mar | Sondin: drawings | 19339 | 450.00 | | 450.00 |
| | | | 27–Mar | Wages and salaries (see analysis below) | 19340 | 10,480.05 | | 10,480.05 |
| | | | 31–Mar | Balance c/d | | 8,806.42 | | |
| 30,590.05 | 25,555.33 | | | | | 30,590.05 | 10,353.58 | 11,430.05 |
| 8,806.42 | | | 1–Apr | Balance b/d | | | | |
| | | | | Wages and salaries analysis | | | | |
| | | | | Direct labour | | | | 6,014.73 |
| | | | | Admin overhead | | | | 1,105.69 |
| | | | | Factory overhead | | | | 1,931.75 |
| | | | | Sell and dist overhead | | | | 1,427.88 |
| | | | | | | | | 10,480.05 |

needed for Task 5

# BANK RECONCILIATION STATEMENT

needed for Tasks 7,11,12

## EXTENDED TRIAL BALANCE

| account name | ledger balances | |
|---|---|---|
| | Dr £ | Cr £ |
| | | |
| | | |
| | | |
| | | |
| | | |
| | | |
| | | |
| | | |
| | | |
| | | |
| | | |
| | | |
| | | |
| | | |
| | | |
| | | |
| | | |
| | | |
| | | |
| | | |
| | | |
| | | |
| | | |
| | | |
| | | |
| | | |
| | | |
| | | |
| | | |
| | | |
| | | |
| | | |
| | | |
| | | |
| | | |
| | | |
| | | |
| | | |
| | | |
| | | |
| | | |
| | | |

name _____ date _____

| adjustments | | profit and loss | | balance sheet | |
|---|---|---|---|---|---|
| Dr £ | Cr £ | Dr £ | Cr £ | Dr £ | Cr £ |
| | | | | | |
| | | | | | |
| | | | | | |
| | | | | | |
| | | | | | |
| | | | | | |
| | | | | | |
| | | | | | |
| | | | | | |
| | | | | | |
| | | | | | |
| | | | | | |
| | | | | | |
| | | | | | |
| | | | | | |
| | | | | | |
| | | | | | |
| | | | | | |
| | | | | | |
| | | | | | |
| | | | | | |
| | | | | | |
| | | | | | |
| | | | | | |
| | | | | | |
| | | | | | |
| | | | | | |
| | | | | | |
| | | | | | |
| | | | | | |
| | | | | | |
| | | | | | |
| | | | | | |
| | | | | | |
| | | | | | |
| | | | | | |
| | | | | | |
| | | | | | |
| | | | | | |
| | | | | | |

needed for Task 8

needed for Task 9

## JOURNAL

| date | account name and narrative | debit £ | credit £ |
|------|----------------------------|---------|----------|
|      |                            |         |          |
|      |                            |         |          |

**data for Task 10**

**Stock of raw materials as at 31 March 1998**

|  | Cost £ | Net realisable value £ |
|---|---|---|
| Material X | 3,417.22 | 3,817.66 |
| Material Y | 5,441.08 | 4,719.33 |

**Finished mendips**

A total of 25,613 units were produced in the year ended 31 March 1998, of which 3,117 units remained in stock at the year end.

**data for Task 11**

**Accruals and prepayments at 31 March 1998**

Branson & Co do not attempt to calculate accruals and prepayments for immaterial amounts, defined as being anything less than £200.

The only two items which may amount to more than this are included in administration overheads, as follows:

- Office rental of £3,250 was paid in December 1997 in respect of the six months ending 30 June 1998.

- Telephone and fax charges amount to about £630 per quarter. At 31 March 1998 these charges had already been paid for the quarter ended 31 January 1998, but the invoice for the subsequent quarter is not expected to arrive until May 1998.

**needed for Task 10**

# Simulation 2
## Harvey & Company

suggested time limit 2 hours

## SCENARIO

This simulation is based on Neil Harvey's sole trader business which sells mobile telephones. The following tasks are undertaken by the accounts assistant, Kim Barnett:

- correction of errors
- extending the trial balance
- explaining the correction of errors
- preparing control accounts
- calculating the cost of stock which has been stolen
- justifying the method of stock valuation

## NVQ UNIT 4 – ELEMENTS COVERED

1   maintain records relating to capital acquisition and disposal
2   record income and expenditure
3   collect and collate information for the preparation of final accounts
4   prepare the extended trial balance

# SIMULATION HARVEY & COMPANY

**2**

## THE SITUATION

Your name is Kim Barnett and you work as the accounts assistant for the firm Harvey and Company which is a retailing outlet specialising in the sale of mobile telephones. The business is owned by Neil Harvey and one of your main duties is the preparation of the accounts in readiness for checking by the Financial Controller, Chris Adams. Chris also acts as your line manager. There is another person who works as part of the accounts team: Martin Speight, who has recently joined as an accounts trainee.

This simulation relates to Harvey and Company's accounting year to 31 March 1999, today's date being 14 April 1999. The company maintains a full system of ledger accounts in manual format, and is registered for VAT, all telephone sales being standard rated.

The Simulation is divided into two sections. There are four tasks relating to section 1 and a similar four tasks relating to section 2.

You are allowed 2 hours to complete the tasks in both sections. You are advised to spend approximately 60 minutes on each section.

## SECTION 1 DATA

A list of balances have been provided, and written into the opening columns of the Extended Trial Balance. At present the opening trial balance does not agree; the difference has been posted to a suspense account. On investigating the ledger and the books of prime entry, you discover the following errors and omissions have been made:

(a) An insurance refund for £240 has been correctly debited in the cash book, but not posted to the insurance account in the ledger.

(b) The Drawings account totalling £5,564 for the year has been completely omitted from the list of balances.

(c) A receipt from a credit customer Mr D Bird has been debited in the cash book with £4,500 and then debited again in his personal account in the sales ledger.

(d) A second-hand delivery van was purchased during the year for £3,000 (net) and this has inadvertently been posted to the Motor Expenses account.

(e) Some packaging costing a total of £140 would be better described as printing and stationery expenses.

(f) The trial balance drawn up does not include the cash sales for the last day of the financial period which were banked late in the afternoon; the total receipts amounted to £3,525 inclusive of VAT.

(g) A payment to a supplier by cheque for £3,000 has been credited in the bank account, but no corresponding debit entry has been made.

## SECTION 1 TASKS

**1.1** Prepare journal entries (narratives not required) on the journal form provided on page 164.

**1.2** Prepare a suspense account (page 165) showing the opening balance as per the original trial balance and the adjustments made with regard to the journal entries prepared as part of Task 1.1 above.

**1.3** Enter the journal entries calculated in Task 1.1 into the adjustments columns contained in the extended trial balance (page 167). Then extend the rows across to prepare a corrected trial balance.

**1.4** Certain errors occur in book-keeping which will not affect the balancing of a trial balance. Some of these errors were seen in Task 1 above. Briefly outline any four such errors which can be undetected in the book-keeping process for the benefit of the new accounts trainee, Martin Speight. Use the memorandum form on page 168.

needed for Task 1.1

## JOURNAL

|     | Details | Dr £ | Cr £ |
| --- | --- | --- | --- |
| (a) | | | |
| (b) | | | |
| (c) | | | |
| (d) | | | |
| (e) | | | |
| (f) | | | |
| (g) | | | |

**needed for Task 1.2**

Dr                                    SUSPENSE ACCOUNT                                    Cr

| Date | Details | Amount | Date | Details | Amount |
|------|---------|--------|------|---------|--------|
|      |         | £      | 1999<br>1 April | Balance b/d | £<br>676 |
|      |         |        |      |         |        |

**needed for Task 1.3**

# EXTENDED TRIAL BALANCE

| account name | ledger balances | |
|---|---|---|
| | Dr £ | Cr £ |
| Advertising | 3,245 | |
| Administration expenses | 6,450 | |
| Bad debts | 2,000 | |
| Bank charges & Interest | 2,456 | |
| Cleaning costs | 8,500 | |
| Discounts Allowed | 3,112 | |
| Discounts received | | 5,788 |
| Entertaining | 2,459 | |
| General expenses | 884 | |
| Insurance | 4,890 | |
| Motor expenses | 12,782 | |
| Packaging costs | 2,540 | |
| Purchases | 86,312 | |
| Printing and stationery | 1,667 | |
| Rates | 3,330 | |
| Salaries | 32,600 | |
| Sales | | 233,451 |
| Wages | 18,342 | |
| Buildings at cost | 60,000 | |
| Depreciation - Buildings | | 12,000 |
| Motor vehicles at cost | 28,000 | |
| Depreciation - Vehicles | | 14,000 |
| Fixtures & Fittings at cost | 35,000 | |
| Depreciation - Fixtures etc. | | 10,500 |
| Stock at 01.04.98 | 67,983 | |
| Debtors | 24,000 | |
| Provision for doubtful debts | | 3,600 |
| Bank | | 5,324 |
| Cash in hand | 600 | |
| Trade Creditors | | 12,165 |
| VAT Account | | 8,765 |
| Inland Revenue | | 2,883 |
| Capital account | | 98,000 |
| Suspense Account | | 676 |
| | | |
| | | |
| | 407,152 | 407,152 |

**needed for Task 1.3**

| account name | adjustments | | corrected trial balance | |
|---|---|---|---|---|
| | Dr £ | Cr £ | Dr £ | Cr £ |
| Advertising | | | | |
| Administration expenses | | | | |
| Bad debts | | | | |
| Bank charges & Interest | | | | |
| Cleaning costs | | | | |
| Discounts Allowed | | | | |
| Discounts received | | | | |
| Entertaining | | | | |
| General expenses | | | | |
| Insurance | | | | |
| Motor expenses | | | | |
| Packaging costs | | | | |
| Purchases | | | | |
| Printing and stationery | | | | |
| Rates | | | | |
| Salaries | | | | |
| Sales | | | | |
| Wages | | | | |
| Buildings at cost | | | | |
| Depreciation - Buildings | | | | |
| Motor vehicles at cost | | | | |
| Depreciation - Vehicles | | | | |
| Fixtures & Fittings at cost | | | | |
| Depreciation - Fixtures etc. | | | | |
| Stock at 01.04.98 | | | | |
| Debtors | | | | |
| Provision for doubtful debts | | | | |
| Bank | | | | |
| Cash in hand | | | | |
| Trade Creditors | | | | |
| VAT Account | | | | |
| Inland Revenue | | | | |
| Capital account | | | | |
| Suspense Account | | | | |
| Drawings | | | | |

needed for Task 1.4

# MEMORANDUM

**To:**

**From:**

**Subject:**                                              **Date:**

**needed for Task 1.4**

## SECTION 2 DATA

You have just heard that there was a theft of stock from the warehouse last night (13 April 1999) but it is not clear how much has been stolen. Chris Adams has asked you to estimate what has been taken so that an insurance claim can be made straightaway. No double-entry records have been written up for April as yet because everyone is still involved with the year-end procedures. However, the following information is available:

|  | as at 1 April 1999 | as at 13 April 1999 |
|---|---|---|
|  | £ | £ |
| Stock at Cost | 67,983 |  |
| Trade Creditors | 9,165 | 13,465 |
| Trade Debtors | 15,000 | 18,250 |

The following transactions have been summarised from the cash book from 1 April 1999 to 13 April 1999.

|  | £ |
|---|---|
| Cash Purchases | 1,450 |
| Paid to Creditors | 5,750 |
| Received from Debtors | 16,560 |
| Cash Sales | 2,230 |
| Discount Allowed | 856 |
| Discount Received | 575 |

On 14 April 1999, before trading recommenced, a quick stock take was made based on the goods which were left in the warehouse after the raid. These are estimated to be worth £45,000 at cost.

Harvey and Company has a pricing policy of applying a mark-up of 50% on the cost of mobile telephones purchased.

## SECTION 2 TASKS

**2.1**   Prepare a creditors control account and ascertain the value of purchases made on credit for the period 1 April 1999 to 13 April 1999. A control account for completion is on page 172.

**2.2**   Prepare a debtors control account for the same period, to calculate the credit sales figure. A blank control form is reproduced on page 172.

**2.3**   Calculate the cost of the stock stolen so that the correct insurance claim can be made by Harvey & Company. You can use the pro-forma trading account displayed on page 173.

**2.4**   Since performing the calculations and assessment in Task 2.3 Martin Speight approaches you and asks:

*"Why can't the insurance claim submitted to the brokers be calculated on its sales value rather than cost. After all, Harvey and Co. would have been able to sell all these telephones at retail price and not at the price at which they bought them."*

Construct a suitable reply to Martin on the Memorandum provided on page 174. Your comments should relate to relevant accounting concepts and SSAP's.

Dr                    **CREDITORS' CONTROL ACCOUNT**                    Cr

| Date | Details | Amount | Date | Details | Amount |
|------|---------|--------|------|---------|--------|
|      |         | £      |      |         | £      |
|      |         |        |      |         |        |

**needed for Task 2.1**

Dr                    **DEBTORS' CONTROL ACCOUNT**                    Cr

| Date | Details | Amount | Date | Details | Amount |
|------|---------|--------|------|---------|--------|
|      |         | £      |      |         | £      |
|      |         |        |      |         |        |

**needed for Task 2.2**

**needed for Task 2.3**

## TRADING ACCOUNT FOR THE PERIOD 1 APRIL 1999 TO 13 APRIL 1999

|  | £ | £ | £ |
|---|---|---|---|
| Cash Sales | | ☐ | |
| Credit Sales | | ☐ | |
| | | | ☐ |
| **Cost of Sales** | | | |
| Opening Stock | | ☐ | |
| Cash Purchases | ☐ | | |
| Credit Purchases | ☐ | | |
| | | ☐ | |
| *less* Closing Stock | | ☐ | |
| | | | ☐ |
| **Gross Profit** | | | ☐ |

needed for Task 2.4

# MEMORANDUM

**To:**

**From:**

**Subject:**                                        **Date:**

# Simulation 3
## Cooper & Mason

suggested time limit 3 hours

## SCENARIO

This simulation is based on work carried out at Cooper & Mason, a firm of accountants. The tasks involve dealing with four clients:

- Rashid Lateef – adjusting for accruals and prepayments
- Andrew Roberts – correction of errors, incomplete records
- Old Malvernians Cricket Club – preparation of club accounts
- Stimpson, Orton and Jameson – partners' current account

## NVQ UNIT 4 – ELEMENTS COVERED

1   maintain records relating to capital acquisition and disposal
2   record income and expenditure
3   collect and collate information for the preparation of final accounts

# SIMULATION COOPER & MASON

*3*

## THE SITUATION

You are employed by a firm of Accountants, Cooper and Mason, as a trainee. Your duties predominantly involve the preparation of final accounts from incomplete records. You also perform other duties such as external audit work and basic book-keeping. Your line manager at work is the senior Accounts Clerk, Leslie Dawson.

## CLIENT 1 – RASHID LATEEF

Today's date is 24 May 1999 and one of your clients, Rashid Lateef has just submitted his ledger, which will need adjusting for the relevant accruals and prepayments.

Rashid owns a window cleaning business and his accounts are usually relatively straightforward to prepare.

Set out below is a list of expenditure Rashid has incurred during the year, together with a list of opening and closing balances.

Rashid's accounting year end is 31 March.

Rashid is not registered for VAT purposes as his annual turnover is below the current threshold.

### RENT PAYABLE

Rashid rents a lock-up garage, a place in which he can store his van and ladders overnight. Rashid pays for the garage quarterly in advance. At 1 April 1998 Rashid had already paid in advance for the two months to 31 May 1998, a total of £300. The agreement is re-negotiated each year on 1 March.

During the year the business paid the following quarterly instalments:

|  |  | £ |
|---|---|---|
| 2 June 1998 | By cheque (to 31 August 1998) | 450 |
| 1 September 1998 | By cheque (to 30 November 1998) | 450 |
| 7 December 1998 | By cheque (to 28 February 1999) | 450 |
| 6 March 1999 | By cheque (to 31 May 1999) | 525 |

### PUBLIC LIABILITY INSURANCE

Rashid pays for his insurance quarterly in arrears. He has signed a direct debit mandate to ensure he keeps his account up-to-date at all times. The renewal date of the policy is 1 November each year.

At the start of this accounting year Rashid owed two months' payments totalling £60.

During the year the following quarterly payments were made:   £

|                  |                |     |
|------------------|----------------|-----|
| 1 May 1998       | by direct debit | 90  |
| 2 August 1998    | by direct debit | 90  |
| 1 November 1998  | by direct debit | 90  |
| 1 February 1999  | by direct debit | 105 |

**You are to** write up the nominal ledger accounts for Rashid Lateef showing clearly the opening and closing balances, the amounts paid during the year as well as the correct transfers to be made to the profit and loss account. You can use the nominal ledger accounts printed below.

Dr        **RENT PAYABLE ACCOUNT**        Cr

| Date | Details | Amount £ | Date | Details | Amount £ |
|------|---------|----------|------|---------|----------|
|      |         |          |      |         |          |

Dr        **PUBLIC LIABILITY INSURANCE ACCOUNT**        Cr

| Date | Details | Amount £ | Date | Details | Amount £ |
|------|---------|----------|------|---------|----------|
|      |         |          |      |         |          |

## CLIENT 2 - ANDREW ROBERTS

One of your colleagues at work is trying to reconcile the Sales Ledger Control account to the debtor balances, but unfortunately he is not having much luck. This tends to be a perennial problem as the client Mr Andrew Roberts does not always balance his books off properly. Often the telephone rings or he is suddenly called out of the office on emergency business, and as a consequence he forgets what he has completed in the ledger and this is where things start to get messy.

Below are the figures from the Sales Ledger Control account, as supplied by a colleague.

### SALES LEDGER CONTROL ACCOUNT FOR THE YEAR TO 28 FEBRUARY 1999

|  | £ |  | £ |
|---|---|---|---|
| Balance b/d | 138,870 | Debtor receipts | 449,817 |
| Credit Sales | 478,110 | Discount Allowed | 19,053 |
|  |  | Returns Inwards | 5,115 |
|  |  | Bad Debts written off | 7,977 |
|  |  | Purchase ledger Contra | 74,274 |
|  |  | Balance c/d | 60,744 |
|  | 616,980 |  | 616,980 |
| Balance b/d | 60,744 |  |  |

You have also received a list of individual customer balances, which have been supplied directly by Mr Roberts, and these total £30,338. However, a thorough check on the book-keeping reveals the following errors and omissions:

1   One of the pages in the sales day book has been added up incorrectly, the total being carried forward as £52,334 instead of the correct amount of £25,334

2   Certain bad debts had been written off in the control account, but no entries had been made in the individual list of balances. The bad debts which needed adjusting totalled £2,412.

3   A debtor balance of £5,668 had been completely omitted from the list of individual customer balances.

4   A cash refund of £3,450 given to a customer CRK Ltd for faulty goods supplied had been adjusted for on the individual list of balances but no entry has been made in the Sales Ledger Control account.

5   An individual customer account Explore PLC has been extracted as a debit balance of £13,740 instead of the correct amount of £17,340.

**You are to**

**2.1**   Make any adjustments that you think are necessary in order to reconcile the Sales Ledger Control account against the individual list of customer balances. Use the blank forms on the next page.

**2.2**   For a good number of years now you have been encouraging Mr Roberts to convert from a manual book-keeping system to a computerised one. Draft a letter to Mr Roberts explaining the advantages such a system could bring to his business. Use the letter heading on page 180.

**needed for Task 2.1**

| Dr | | | | SALES LEDGER CONTROL ACCOUNT | | Cr |
|---|---|---|---|---|---|---|
| Date | Details | Amount | Date | Details | | Amount |
| | | £ | 1999 1 April | Balance b/d | | £ 676.00 |

**needed for Task 2.1**

**CUSTOMER BALANCES LISTING**

needed for Task 2.2

# COOPER & MASON, ACCOUNTANTS

14 Leigh Brook Road
Upper Hatherley
Cheltenham GL52 4RR
Tel 01242 576042  Fax 01242 567424

Partners: Terry Cooper and Gary Mason

## CLIENT 3 – THE OLD MALVERNIANS CRICKET CLUB

A new set of books has just come into the office of Cooper & Mason and the financial statements need preparing. They are from the Old Malvernians Cricket Club (OMCC). Cooper and Mason are the official accountants for the club and they also act as external auditors.

Set out below is a summary of the OMCC cash book for the year ended 31 December 1998.

| RECEIPTS | £ | PAYMENTS | £ |
|---|---|---|---|
| Balance at bank b/d | 5,410 | 250 Club expenses | 1,300 |
| Bar sales | 29,134 | Extension to pavilion | 8,940 |
| Match fees | 950 | Rates on buildings | 1,520 |
| Members' subscriptions | 5,675 | Electricity | 2,134 |
| Donations received | 800 | Groundsman's Wages | 6,250 |
| Gaming Machine receipts | 6,780 | Printing & stationery | 569 |
| Annual Dinner Dance receipts | 3,775 | Accountancy | 500 |
| 250 Club receipts | 2,900 | Dinner Dance expenses | 3,660 |
| Life Membership | 1,000 | Telephone | 313 |
| | | Bar suppliers | 15,334 |
| | | New Mower | 2,345 |
| | | Bar staff wages | 4,875 |
| | | Gaming machine rent | 2,600 |
| | | Balance at bank c/d | 6,084 |
| | 56,424 | | 56,424 |
| Balance at bank b/d | 6,084 | | |

You have also been given the following information relating to balances at the start and the end of the year:

| | 31 December 1997 £ | 31 December 1998 £ |
|---|---|---|
| Bar Supplier creditor | 4,680 | 5,835 |
| Accruals for electricity | 187 | 209 |
| Prepaid rates | 320 | 400 |
| Subscriptions in arrears | 50 | 150 |
| Subscriptions in advance | 150 | 200 |
| Bar stock | 3,639 | 4,926 |
| Land and buildings | 32,000 | |
| Life Membership fund | 4,000 | |
| Cricket equipment at NBV | 2,230 | |
| Clubhouse furniture at NBV | 8,600 | |

## ADDITIONAL INFORMATION

It is the Cricket Club's policy to depreciate it's assets on the following basis:

| | |
|---|---|
| Buildings | 10% |
| Cricket Equipment | 25% |
| Clubhouse Furniture | 20% |

All rates are based on the reduced balance method, ie on the book value brought forward from the previous year.

It is also policy that all charges for depreciation are rounded up to the nearest whole pound and the club charges a full year's depreciation in the year of acquisition, irrespective of the time of purchase. No depreciation is taken in the year of sale.

With regard to the land and buildings only the buildings are depreciated. The valuation brought forward of £32,000 can be split between Land at Cost £25,000 and Buildings at NBV £7,000.

It is the Club's policy to introduce the Life membership scheme on the accounting basis of income received over a 10 year period: each year the balance of the life membership fund (old and new memberships) is written down by a flat 10%, and this 10% is treated as income in the accounts.

**You are to**

**3.1** Prepare an Income and Expenditure account for the year to 31 December 1998, showing clearly the surplus/deficit for the year. You may use the format shown on the opposite page.

**3.2** Prepare a balance sheet as at 31 December 1998. You may use the format shown on page 184.

**3.3** The cricket club has had a major upsurge in membership in recent years, mainly due to the club's success on the playing field. The committee are now thinking of charging any new members a one-off entrance fee to join the club similar to golf clubs in the region. This will be in addition to any annual subscription. The treasurer is unsure as to how such fees should be recorded in the club's accounts.

On the memorandum on page 185 explain to the Treasurer the correct accounting treatment for the cricket club with regard to 'Entrance fees'.

needed for Task 3.1

THE OLD MALVERNIANS CRICKET CLUB
INCOME AND EXPENDITURE ACCOUNT FOR THE YEAR TO 31 DECEMBER 1998

Income                                    £                              £

Expenditure

Surplus/(Deficit) for the year

needed for Task 3.2

# THE OLD MALVERNIANS CRICKET CLUB
## BALANCE SHEET AS AT 31 DECEMBER 1998

|  | £ | £ | £ |
|---|---|---|---|
| FIXED ASSETS | | | |
| CURRENT ASSETS | | | |
| CURRENT LIABILITIES | | | |
| NET CURRENT ASSETS | | | |
| REPRESENTED BY: ACCUMULATED FUND | | | |
| LIFE MEMBERSHIP FUND | | | |

needed for Task 3.3

# MEMORANDUM

**To:**

**From:**

**Subject:**                                                    **Date:**

## CLIENT 4 – STIMPSON, ORTON AND JAMESON

Finally, a rushed job has just been passed on to you for completion. This relates to the partnership of Stimpson, Orton and Jameson who share profits and losses in the ratio of 2/5, 2/5 and 1/5 respectively.

The net profit of the business for the year to 31 January 1999 has been calculated as £90,400. The following balances have been brought forward from last years balance sheet:

|  | Capital Account £ | Current Account £ |  |
|---|---|---|---|
| Stimpson | 60,000 | 4,250 | Credit |
| Orton | 75,000 | 1,250 | Debit |
| Jameson | 55,000 | 2,345 | Credit |

You have ascertained from the business cash book and ledger that the following drawings were made by the partners:

|  | £ |
|---|---|
| Stimpson | 25,000 |
| Orton | 29,000 |
| Jameson | 19,500 |

**You are to**

Prepare from the information available the partners' current accounts for the year. You can use the blank pro-forma set out below. Use the left-hand side for debit entries and the right-hand side for credit entries.

Dr.                                                                                                                  Cr.

| Stimpson £ | Orton £ | Jameson £ |  | Stimpson £ | Orton £ | Jameson £ |
|---|---|---|---|---|---|---|
|  |  |  | Balance b/d |  |  |  |
|  |  |  | Profit Share |  |  |  |
|  |  |  | Drawings |  |  |  |
|  |  |  | Balance c/d |  |  |  |
|  |  |  |  |  |  |  |
|  |  |  | Balance b/d |  |  |  |

# Central Assessment Tasks

## Creative Catering

reproduced by kind permission of AAT

recommended timing 3 hours

## NOTE TO STUDENTS

This assessment has been issued by AAT to provide guidance for students completing Central Assessments following the 1998 revision in Level 3 specifications.

The Assessment is divided into three sections.

The recommended timing is as follows:

| | |
|---|---|
| Section 1 | 80 minutes |
| Section 2 | 40 minutes |
| Section 3 | 60 minutes |

Please note that from December 1999 the Central Assessment will be set out in two sections. The content and approach will remain the same.

# SECTION 1

**You are recommended to spend 80 minutes carrying out the tasks in this Section.**

Jane Sutton is the proprietor of Creative Catering, a firm that provides catering services for a variety of events and functions. Creative Catering's premises are located in Bristol and most of the firm's customers can be found in the west of England.

You are employed by Jane Sutton to assist with the book-keeping.

The business currently operates a manual system consisting of a general ledger, a sales ledger and a purchases ledger.

Double-entry takes place in the general ledger and the individual accounts of debtors and creditors are therefore regarded as memoranda accounts.

Day books consisting of a purchases day book, a sales day book, a purchases returns day book and a sales returns day book are used. Totals from the various columns of the day books are transferred periodically into the general ledger.

At the end of the financial year on 30 April 1998, the balances were extracted from the general ledger and entered into an extended trial balance as shown on page 189.

**Task 1.1**

**Make appropriate entries in the adjustment columns of the extended trial balance to take account of the following:**

(a) The stock consists of food and drink and has been valued on 30 April 1988 at £6,240. This figure includes some frozen food that had cost £860 but will have to be thrown out due to a problem with a freezer. Although the Polar Insurance Company has agreed to pay for the full cost of the food, no money has yet been received. Also included in the stock valuation figure are 20 bottles of wine. These had originally cost £8.50 each but since they are not popular they are to be sold off at £6.50 per bottle.

(b) Depreciation calculated on a monthly basis is to be provided as follows:
Motor Vehicles: 20% per annum straight line method
Equipment: 10% per annum reducing balance method

(c) The sum of £20,000 was invested in the bank deposit account on 1 May 1997. The interest rate is fixed at 7% per annum.

(d) Rent payable by the business is as follows:
Up to 31 October 1997: £1,200 per month
From 1 November 1997: £1,300 per month

(e) The provision for bad debts is to be adjusted to a figure representing 5% of debtors.

(f) On 29 April 1998 Jane Sutton withdrew £5,000 from the bank account for her own use. The entries made were:
Debit Cash £5,000
Credit Bank £5,000

(g) A series of adverts was broadcast during April 1998 by Western Radio at a cost to Creative Catering of £2,750. The invoice has yet to be received from Western Radio and no entries have been made.

**Extended Trial Balance at 30 April 1998**

| DESCRIPTION | LEDGER BALANCES | | ADJUSTMENTS | |
|---|---|---|---|---|
| | Dr | Cr | Dr | Cr |
| | £ | £ | £ | £ |
| Sales | | 620,700 | | |
| Purchases | 410,650 | | | |
| Purchases returns | | 390 | | |
| Salaries and wages | 90,820 | | | |
| Rent | 16,300 | | | |
| Debtors control account | 51,640 | | | |
| Creditors control account | | 33,180 | | |
| Bad debts | 6,650 | | | |
| Provision for bad debts | | 3,100 | | |
| Motor Vehicles (M.V.) at cost | 60,700 | | | |
| Provision for depreciation (M.V.) | | 12,600 | | |
| Equipment (Equip) at cost | 24,200 | | | |
| Provision for depreciation (Equip) | | 6,300 | | |
| Drawings | 28,500 | | | |
| Cash | 7,000 | | | |
| Bank | 6,250 | | | |
| Lighting and Heating | 2,100 | | | |
| Insurance | 760 | | | |
| Advertising | 3,470 | | | |
| VAT (credit balance) | | 8,400 | | |
| Stock at 1 May 1997 | 5,000 | | | |
| Motor expenses | 4,680 | | | |
| Bank deposit account | 20,000 | | | |
| Bank interest received | | 700 | | |
| Capital | | 54,010 | | |
| | | | | |
| Prepayments | | | | |
| Polar Insurance Company | | | | |
| Depreciation | | | | |
| Closing stock-P & L | | | | |
| Closing stock-Balance sheet | | | | |
| Provision for bad debts-Adjustment | | | | |
| Deposit account interest owing | | | | |
| Accrued expenses | | | | |
| | 739,380 | 739,380 | | |

Note: only the above columns of the extended trial balance are required for this Assessment.

The bank statement shown below was received by Creative Catering on 1 June 1998 and was compared with the bank account section of the cash book also shown below.

<table>
<tr><td colspan="5" align="center">**MIDWEST BANK LTD**<br>**Bank Statement**</td></tr>
<tr><td colspan="3">**Account:** Creative Catering</td><td colspan="2">**Account Number:** 60419776</td></tr>
<tr><td>**Date**</td><td>**Detail**</td><td>**Debit**</td><td>**Credit**</td><td>**Balance**</td></tr>
<tr><td>1998</td><td></td><td>£</td><td>£</td><td>£</td></tr>
<tr><td>14 May</td><td>Balance</td><td></td><td></td><td>6,300</td></tr>
<tr><td>14 May</td><td>Cheque 606842</td><td>120</td><td></td><td>6,180</td></tr>
<tr><td>14 May</td><td>Bank Giro Credit</td><td></td><td>230</td><td>6,410</td></tr>
<tr><td>15 May</td><td>Credit</td><td></td><td>320</td><td>6,730</td></tr>
<tr><td>18 May</td><td>Cheque 606844</td><td>260</td><td></td><td>6,470</td></tr>
<tr><td>19 May</td><td>Cheque 606843</td><td>440</td><td></td><td>6,030</td></tr>
<tr><td>20 May</td><td>Credit</td><td></td><td>375</td><td>6,405</td></tr>
<tr><td>21 May</td><td>Credit</td><td></td><td>2,650</td><td>9,055</td></tr>
<tr><td>22 May</td><td>Cheque 606846</td><td>1,100</td><td></td><td>7,955</td></tr>
<tr><td>22 May</td><td>Credit</td><td></td><td>860</td><td>8,815</td></tr>
<tr><td>26 May</td><td>Cheque 606848</td><td>1,650</td><td></td><td>7,165</td></tr>
<tr><td>27 May</td><td>Cheque</td><td>470</td><td></td><td>6,695</td></tr>
<tr><td>28 May</td><td>Credit</td><td></td><td>1,950</td><td>8,645</td></tr>
</table>

**Bank Account**

| | | | | | | | |
|---|---|---|---|---|---|---|---|
| May 15 | Balance b/d | | 5,800 | May 16 | J Champion | 845 | 620 |
| 18 | P Donald | | 175 | 16 | Catering Services | 846 | 1,100 |
| 18 | Mayes Ltd | | 200 | 20 | Witworth Drinks | 847 | 490 |
| 19 | A Palmer | | 230 | 20 | K J Foods | 848 | 1,650 |
| 19 | Rugby Club | | 1,260 | 22 | D Andrews | 849 | 470 |
| 20 | Town Institute | | 1,390 | 26 | Catering Services | 850 | 260 |
| 22 | P Whelan | | 860 | 27 | Days Bakery | 851 | 320 |
| 25 | P Whitehead | | 1,950 | 29 | K J Foods | 852 | 1,400 |
| 28 | Tennis Club | | 1,810 | 29 | Balance c/d | | 7,365 |
| | | | 13,675 | | | | 13,675 |

**Task 1.2**

Prepare a statement reconciling the £5,800 opening balance of the cash book with the £6,300 opening balance of the bank statement.

**Task. 1.3**

Prepare a bank reconciliation statement as at 29 May 1998.

## SECTION 2

**You are recommended to spend 40 minutes carrying out the tasks in this Section.**

Answer each of the following tasks in the space provided as clearly and concisely as you can or, where appropriate, circle the correct answer.

**2.1**    One of the vans used by Creative Catering was originally purchased on 1 November 1995 for £12,360.  If the van was sold on 1 June 1998 for £6,500:

(a) What would be the book value of the van at the date of sale?


£.............................

(b) What would be the profit or loss on disposal of the van?


£............................. profit/loss

**2.2**    Jane Sutton is a member of the local golf club and occasionally assists with the club accounts.  For the year to 31 December 1997 the club had 380 members.  On 1 January 1997 six members owed the subscription for the previous year, but all of them subsequently paid the amount owing (£250 per member).  At this time, no subscriptions were prepaid.  On 31 December 1997 ten members had prepaid their subscription for the following year (£250 per member).  During the year ended 31 December 1997, £98,000 was received in subscriptions.  The amount payable for the year was again £250 per member.

Calculate the number of members who had not paid their subscription on 31 December 1997.

. . . . . . . . . . . . . . . . . . . . . . . . . . . . . . . . . . . . . . . . . . . . . . . . . . . . . . . . . . . . .

. . . . . . . . . . . . . . . . . . . . . . . . . . . . . . . . . . . . . . . . . . . . . . . . . . . . . . . . . . . . .

. . . . . . . . . . . . . . . . . . . . . . . . . . . . . . . . . . . . . . . . . . . . . . . . . . . . . . . . . . . . .

. . . . . . . . . . . . . . . . . . . . . . . . . . . . . . . . . . . . . . . . . . . . . . . . . . . . . . . . . . . . .

. . . . . . . . . . . . . . . . . . . . . . . . . . . . . . . . . . . . . . . . . . . . . . . . . . . . . . . . . . . . .

. . . . . . . . . . . . . . . . . . . . . . . . . . . . . . . . . . . . . . . . . . . . . . . . . . . . . . . . . . . . .

. . . . . . . . . . . . . . . . . . . . . . . . . . . . . . . . . . . . . . . . . . . . . . . . . . . . . . . . . . . . .

. . . . . . . . . . . . . . . . . . . . . . . . . . . . . . . . . . . . . . . . . . . . . . . . . . . . . . . . . . . . .

. . . . . . . . . . . . . . . . . . . . . . . . . . . . . . . . . . . . . . . . . . . . . . . . . . . . . . . . . . . . .

. . . . . . . . . . . . . . . . . . . . . . . . . . . . . . . . . . . . . . . . . . . . . . . . . . . . . . . . . . . . .

**2.3**  Creative Catering provided catering to Barrett & Co, a small local business that is not registered for VAT.  The sales invoice issued to Barrett & Co shows a total sum of £329, which includes £49 VAT. Barrett & Co treats the invoice as a hospitality expense in its books.

NOTE: State clearly for both (a) and (b) the names of the accounts, the amounts and whether each entry is a debit or credit.

(a)  What would be the double entry made in Creative Catering's books to record the sale to Barrett & Co?

................................................................................

................................................................................

................................................................................

(b)  What would be the double entry made in Barrett & Co's books to record the purchase from Creative Catering?

................................................................................

................................................................................

................................................................................

**2.4**  Jane Sutton decides to purchase some new equipment for Creative Catering on hire purchase. When does Creative Catering record the equipment as a fixed asset in the books of the business?

(1)  When the equipment is acquired

(2)  When the final instalment is paid

(3)  The equipment is never shown as a fixed asset

**2.5**  A credit sale made to the Bristol Rowing Club is entered in error into the account of the Bristol Rugby Club in the sales ledger.

(a)  Would the error be detected through the use of the debtors control account?

Yes/No

(b)  Briefly explain the reason for your answer.

................................................................................

................................................................................

................................................................................

................................................................................

................................................................................

**2.6** After the end of the financial year on 30 April 1998 and after the profit for the year has been calculated, an invoice dated 20 April 1998 is found in a pile of letters. The invoice relates to a £500 purchase of soft drinks and has not been entered into the books of Creative Catering. Jane Sutton discusses the matter with you and says that she is concerned that in leaving out the invoice the calculation of the profit figure might have been affected. However, she finally decides that since all the drinks have been included in the valuation of the closing stock, none could have been sold during the year. She is therefore satisfied that all is well from an accounting point of view and tells you "since none of the drinks were included in either the sales or purchases figures, the profits were not affected."

She asks you to think about what she has said and to confirm her conclusions.

Write an appropriate memo to Jane Sutton covering the points she has raised relating to the calculation of profit for the financial year ended 30 April 1998. Use the format shown below.

# MEMO

**To:**                                                        **Ref:**

**From:**                                                    **Date:**

# SECTION 3

**You are recommended to spend 60 minutes carrying out the tasks in this Section.**

Jane Sutton obtains her supplies of bread and cakes mainly from a small bakery owned by Pat Day. The goods are sold to various caterers, retailers and direct to the public through a shop attached to the bakery and also owned by Pat Day. The bakery and the shop have both recently been put up for sale and Jane Sutton is interested in buying them. She has been able to obtain some figures from the agent acting for Pat Day and these relate to the year ended 31 December 1997. Jane Sutton has asked you to produce some information from these figures.

**Figures for Pat Day's bakery and shop – made available by the agent:**

| | £ |
|---|---:|
| ■ STOCKS | |
| Stock of baking materials at 1 January 1997 | 1,000 |
| Baking materials purchased | 84,000 |
| Stock of baking materials at 31 December 1997 | 3,000 |
| All finished goods are sold and no finished goods are therefore held in stock. | |
| ■ STAFF COSTS | |
| Bakery production wages | 44,000 |
| Bakery supervisor wages | 25,000 |
| Shop wages | 30,000 |
| ■ BUSINESS FIXED ASSETS | |
| Bakery premises at cost 1 January 1970 | 100,000 |
| Shop premises at cost 1 January 1970 | 80,000 |
| Bakery equipment at cost 1 June 1990 | 50,000 |
| Shop equipment at cost 1 June 1990 | 40,000 |
| ■ DEPRECIATION - calculated on a monthly basis: | |
| Premises 2% per annum straight line method | |
| Equipment 10% per annum straight line method | |
| ■ OTHER BUSINESS EXPENSES | |
| Bakery overheads | 22,000 |
| Shop expenses | 30,000 |
| ■ SALES | |
| Two thirds of production is sold with a 50% mark-up to caterers and retail outlets. | |
| All these sales are on credit. | |
| One third of production is passed to the shop to then be sold with a 100% mark-up. | |
| All these sales are for cash. | |
| ■ DEBTORS AND CREDITORS | |
| Debtors at 1 January 1997 | 12,000 |
| Creditors at 1 January 1997 | 6,000 |
| Debtors at 31 December 1997 | Unknown |
| Creditors at 31 December 1997 | 7,000 |
| Received from debtors during the year | 179,500 |
| Paid to creditors during the year | Unknown |

**Task 3.1**

Calculate the prime cost of the goods produced by the bakery during the year ended 31 December 1997.

**Task 3.2**

Calculate the total production cost of the goods made by the bakery during the year ended 31 December 1997.

**Task 3.3**

Calculate the total combined gross profit made by the shop and bakery during the year ended 31 December 1997.

**Task 3.4**

Calculate the amount paid to creditors during the year ended 31 December 1997.

**Task 3.5**

Calculate the sum of money owed by debtors on 31 December 1997.

# Central Assessment Tasks

## Colin Drew

reproduced by kind permission of AAT

recommended timing 3 hours

## NOTE TO STUDENTS

This assessment was issued by AAT in December 1997 to cover the Unit 'Preparing Financial Accounts' under the pre-1998 specifications.

These tasks are still relevant to the current specifications, but students should study the structure of the 'Creative Catering' Central Assessment (page 187) for specific guidance for the revised Unit.

The Assessment is divided into three sections.

The recommended timing is as follows:

| | |
|---|---|
| Section 1 | 75 minutes |
| Section 2 | 40 minutes |
| Section 3 | 65 minutes |

Please note that from December 1999 the Central Assessment will be set out in two sections. The content and approach will remain the same.

## SECTION 1

**Suggested time allocation: 75 minutes**

Colin Drew is the proprietor of Drew Installations, a firm specialising in the supply and installation of kitchens and bathrooms. The showroom, warehouse and offices are located in London and most of the work carried out by the business is in the London area.

You are employed by Colin Drew to assist with the book-keeping.

The business currently operates a manual system consisting of a general ledger, a sales ledger and a purchases ledger.

Double-entry takes place in the general ledger and the individual accounts of debtors and creditors are therefore regarded as memoranda accounts.

Daybooks consisting of a purchases daybook, a sales day book, a purchases returns daybook and a sales returns daybook are used. Totals from the various columns of the daybooks are transferred into the general ledger.

At the end of the financial year on 31 October 1997, the balances were extracted from the general ledger and entered into an extended trial balance as shown on page 202.

Unfortunately in preparing the extended trial balance it was found that the total of the debit column did not agree with the total of the credit column. A suspense account was opened as a temporary measure.

### Task 1.1

Make appropriate entries in the adjustment columns of the extended trial balance to take account of the following:

(a)    Depreciation calculated on a monthly basis is to be provided as follows:

Motor vehicles - 20% per annum straight line method
Equipment - 10% per annum reducing balance method

On 30 April 1997 a new motor vehicle costing £12,000 had been purchased.

(b)    The bank loan had originally been taken out on 30 April 1996 when the sum of £60,000 had been borrowed, repayable by six annual repayments of £10,000. The first repayment had been made as agreed on 30 April 1997. Interest is charged on the loan at 8% per annum.

(c)    Rent payable by the business is as follows:
Showroom and offices - £3,000 per month
Warehouse - £2,000 per month

(d)    The motor vehicle expenses include a payment of £260 paid out of the business bank account to service Colin Drew's family car which is not used in the business.

(e)    Insurance includes an annual buildings policy which runs from 1 August 1997. The premium paid was £2,400.

(f)    The provision for bad debts is to be adjusted to a figure representing 8% of debtors.

(g)    Stock has been valued at cost on 31 October 1997 at £107,300. However, this includes some discontinued kitchen cabinets the details of which are as follows:

| | |
|---|---|
| Cost | £2,300 |
| Normal Selling Price | £3,500 |
| Net Realisable Value | £1,800 |

**Task 1.2**

Subsequent to the preparation of the extended trial balance the following errors were found, some of which had caused the opening of the suspense account.

Prepare journal entries to record the correction of the errors using the blank journal on page 203. Dates and narratives are not required.

(a)    The VAT column of the sales returns day book had been overcast by £200.

(b)    Motor vehicle expenses of £40 had been debited to Motor Vehicles (any adjustment to depreciation can be ignored).

(c)    Sales returns of £160 had been credited to purchases returns. The VAT element of the returns had been entered correctly.

(d)    Purchases of £2,340 had been transferred from the net column of the day book and into the purchases account as £2,430.

(e)    A cheque for £2,450 paid to Ashwood Kitchens, a credit supplier, had been entered in the cash book but not in the relevant control account.

## Extended Trial Balance at 31 October 1997

| DESCRIPTION | LEDGER BALANCES | | ADJUSTMENTS | |
|---|---|---|---|---|
| | Dr | Cr | Dr | Cr |
| | £ | £ | £ | £ |
| Purchases | 339,500 | | | |
| Sales | | 693,000 | | |
| Purchases returns | | 6,320 | | |
| Sales returns | 1,780 | | | |
| Carriage Inwards | 8,250 | | | |
| Salaries and Wages | 106,200 | | | |
| Bad Debts | 4,890 | | | |
| Provision for bad debts | | 4,500 | | |
| Debtors control account | 46,800 | | | |
| Creditors control account | | 28,760 | | |
| Stock at 1 November 1996 | 113,450 | | | |
| Motor vehicle expenses | 5,780 | | | |
| Motor Vehicles (M.V.) at cost | 86,000 | | | |
| Provision for depreciation (M.V.) | | 12,800 | | |
| Equipment (Equip) at cost | 24,500 | | | |
| Provision for depreciation (Equip) | | 6,700 | | |
| Rent | 58,000 | | | |
| Drawings | 32,900 | | | |
| Insurance | 5,720 | | | |
| Bank | 8,580 | | | |
| Bank loan account | | 50,000 | | |
| Bank interest paid | 2,400 | | | |
| VAT (credit balance) | | 12,400 | | |
| Capital | | 32,750 | | |
| Suspense account | 2,480 | | | |
| | | | | |
| Prepayments | | | | |
| Depreciation | | | | |
| Closing stock -P&L | | | | |
| Closing stock - Balance sheet | | | | |
| Provision for bad debts - Adjustment | | | | |
| Loan interest owing | | | | |
| Other accruals | | | | |
| | 847,230 | 847,230 | | |

NOTE: Only the above columns of the extended trial balance are required for this central assessment.

| JOURNAL | | |
|---|---|---|
| | Dr £ | Cr £ |
| | | |

# SECTION 2

**Suggested time allocation: 40 minutes**

**Answer each of the following questions in the space provided as clearly and concisely as you can or, where appropriate, circle the correct answer.**

**2.1**  Colin Drew is considering part-exchanging one of the business motor vehicles for a new model. The garage has offered him £2,500 in part-exchange and he will need to pay a further £10,000 by cheque. It has been calculated that the loss on disposal on the old vehicle will be £500. The vehicle was originally purchased at a price of £9,000.

What would have been the total depreciation charge to profits during the life of the asset excluding the loss on disposal?

£.................

**2.2**  Assume that before Colin Drew was registered for VAT, Drew Installations had purchased goods costing £400 plus VAT £70 for cash.

NOTE: State clearly for both (a) and (b) the names of the accounts, the amounts and whether each entry is a debit or credit.

(a)  What would have been the double entry made in Drew Installation's books to record the purchase?

.........................................................................................

.........................................................................................

.........................................................................................

.........................................................................................

(b)  What would have been the double entry made in the seller's books to record the sale to Drew Installations?

.........................................................................................

.........................................................................................

.........................................................................................

.........................................................................................

.........................................................................................

**2.3**    Colin Drew is thinking of manufacturing some of the kitchen cabinets supplied to customers. He estimates that in the first year of production 15,000 units could be made, with sales of 10,000 units. Costs associated with the kitchen cabinets would be as follows:

Direct materials used                        £20,000

Direct labour used                           £5,000

Direct production overheads                  £5,000

Selling and distribution expenses    £3,000

If Colin Drew were to proceed on this basis, what would be the estimated value of the closing stock of 5,000 units?

£..............................

**2.4**    The three figures shown on a sales invoice of £4,080 plus VAT £714, total £4,794, were mistakenly entered in the sales day book of Drew Installations as £4,800 plus VAT £714, total £5,514.

(a)    Would the error be detected by drawing up a trial balance?

Yes/No

(b)    Briefly explain the reason for your answer to (a).

. . . . . . . . . . . . . . . . . . . . . . . . . . . . . . . . . . . . . . . . . . . . . . . . . . . . .

. . . . . . . . . . . . . . . . . . . . . . . . . . . . . . . . . . . . . . . . . . . . . . . . . . . . .

. . . . . . . . . . . . . . . . . . . . . . . . . . . . . . . . . . . . . . . . . . . . . . . . . . . . .

. . . . . . . . . . . . . . . . . . . . . . . . . . . . . . . . . . . . . . . . . . . . . . . . . . . . .

. . . . . . . . . . . . . . . . . . . . . . . . . . . . . . . . . . . . . . . . . . . . . . . . . . . . .

**2.5**    You have received the following note from Colin Drew.

'I have been looking at the valuation of the closing stock prepared for the trial balance and the final accounts. It occurs to me that the current range of deluxe bathroom suites is selling so well that we are almost certain to sell the existing stock. In view of this, if we were to include the stock at selling price the cost of goods sold would effectively be reduced and the gross profit would therefore be increased. I am anxious to show as high a profit as possible and would like to have your thoughts on this proposal'.

Write a suitable response to Colin Drew in the form of a memo. Your answer should include references to the accounting concept of prudence and SSAP9. Use the format on page 206 for your answer.

# MEMO

To:                                    Ref:

From:                                  Date:

# SECTION 3

**Suggested time allocation: 65 minutes**

During Colin Drew's early years in business trading as Drew Installations, he had very little administrative help and kept minimal records.  A number of queries have now arisen and it has become necessary to calculate some figures relating to the year ended 31 October 1992.  You have been asked to provide assistance.  The information available from Drew Installations is as follows:

|  | £ | £ |
|---|---|---|
| ■ ASSETS AT 1 NOVEMBER 1991 | | |
| Stock | | 30,400 |
| Debtors | | 22,800 |
| Motor Vehicles at cost | 8,750 | |
| Less provision for depreciation | 2,690 | |
| | | 6,060 |
| Equipment at cost | 5,200 | |
| Less provision for depreciation | 840 | |
| | | 4,360 |
| ■ LIABILITIES AT 1 NOVEMBER 1991 | | |
| Creditors | | 15,600 |
| Bank overdraft | | 4,300 |
| Accrued expenses | | 1,000 |
| ■ PAYMENTS MADE DURING THE YEAR ENDED 31 OCTOBER 1992 | | |
| To creditors | | 120,750 |
| Expenses | | 52,800 |
| Equipment purchased 30 April 1992 | | 4,500 |
| Drawings | | Unknown |
| ■ RECEIPTS DURING THE YEAR ENDED 31 OCTOBER 1992 | | |
| From debtors | | Unknown |

■ PROFIT MARGIN 50% on all sales.

■ DEPRECIATION calculated on a monthly basis was provided as follows:
Motor vehicles: 20% per annum straight line method
Equipment: 10% per annum reducing balance method

|  | £ |
|---|---|
| ■ ASSETS AT 31 OCTOBER 1992 | |
| Stock | 32,700 |
| Debtors | 21,700 |
| Motor vehicles at cost | 8,750 |
| Equipment at cost | 9,700 |
| Bank | 15,850 |
| Prepaid expenses | 1,500 |
| ■ LIABILITIES AT 31 OCTOBER 1992 | |
| Creditors | 16,850 |

**Task 3.1**

Calculate the cost of goods sold during the year ended 31 October 1992.

**Task 3.2**

Calculate the gross profit for the year ended 31 October 1992.

**Task 3.3**

Calculate the sales for the year ended 31 October 1992.

**Task 3.4**

Calculate the receipts from debtors for the year ended 31 October 1992.

**Task 3.5**

Calculate the drawings made by Colin Drew during the year ended 31 October 1992.

**Task 3.6**

Calculate the net profit for the year ended 31 October 1992.

# Central Assessment Tasks

## Electronics World Limited

reproduced by kind permission of AAT

recommended timing 3 hours

### NOTE TO STUDENTS

This assessment was issued by AAT in June 1997 to cover the Unit 'Preparing Financial Accounts' under the pre-1998 specifications.

These tasks are still relevant to the current specifications, but students should study the structure of the 'Creative Catering' Central Assessment (page 187) for specific guidance for the revised Unit.

The Assessment is divided into three sections.

The recommended timing is as follows:

| | |
|---|---|
| Section 1 | 75 minutes |
| Section 2 | 50 minutes |
| Section 3 | 55 minutes |

Please note that from December 1999 the Central Assessment will be set out in two sections. The content and approach will remain the same.

# SECTION 1

**Suggested time allocation: 75 minutes**

The company Electronics World Ltd operates out of offices and a warehouse located in Wales. The company purchases hi-fi systems, televisions and other electronic goods from manufacturers world-wide. Customers are mainly UK-based shops specialising in electronic items.

You are employed by Electronic World Ltd to assist with the book-keeping.

The company is relatively new and is still considering an appropriate computerised accounting system.

The manual system currently in use consists of a general ledger, a sales ledger and a purchases ledger.

Double-entry takes place in the general ledger and the individual accounts of debtors and creditors are therefore regarded as memoranda accounts.

Day books consisting of a purchases day book, a sales day book, a purchases returns day book and a sales returns day book are used. Totals from the various columns of the day books are transferred periodically into the general ledger.

The following balances were extracted by a colleague from the general ledger on 24 May 1997, one week before the end of the financial year, which is on 31 May 1997.

|  | £ |
|---|---|
| Share Capital | 600,000 |
| Premises | 360,000 |
| Fixtures and Fittings (F and F) at cost | 140,000 |
| Provision for depreciation (F and F) | 65,000 |
| Purchases | 972,140 |
| Sales | 1,530,630 |
| Salaries | 206,420 |
| Sales returns | 23,200 |
| Purchases returns | 17,350 |
| General expenses | 74,322 |
| Insurance | 16,390 |
| Bad debts | 7,506 |
| Provision for bad debts | 6,000 |
| Debtors control account | 237,855 |
| Creditors control account | 121,433 |
| Stock at 1 June 1996 | 188,960 |
| Bank | 65,200 |
| Bank deposit account | 150,000 |
| Bank interest received | 3,750 |
| Motor Vehicles (M.V.) at cost | 22,400 |
| Provision for depreciation (M.V.) | 3,800 |
| VAT (credit balance) | 24,720 |
| Profit and Loss | 91,710 |

During the last week of the financial year a number of transactions took place and these are summarised below:

**Purchases Day Book**

| | Total | VAT | Net |
|---|---|---|---|
| | £ | £ | £ |
| | 23,970 | 3,570 | 20,400 |

**Sales Day Book**

| | Total | VAT | Net |
|---|---|---|---|
| | £ | £ | £ |
| | 35,955 | 5,355 | 30,600 |

**Sales Returns Day Book**

| | Total | VAT | Net |
|---|---|---|---|
| | £ | £ | £ |
| | 1,410 | 210 | 1,200 |

**Cheques Issued**

| | £ |
|---|---|
| Payable to various creditors in settlement of debts | 5,000 |

**Task 1.1**

Complete the table below to show the double entry which would have to be carried out in order to update the balances extracted on 24 May 1997, to take account of the summarised transactions shown on page 213.

| Double Entry to update balances extracted on 24 May 1997 | | |
|---|---|---|
| Names of Accounts | Dr £ | Cr £ |
| Entries from Purchases Day Book: | | |
| Entries from Sales Day Book: | | |
| Entries from Sales Returns Day Book: | | |
| Entries from Cheques issued: | | |

**Task 1.2**

Enter the updated balances into the first two columns of the extended trial balance provided on page 216. Total the two columns ensuring that the two totals agree.

Note: it is the updated balances that should be used, taking into account the effects of the entries prepared for Task 1.1.

**Task 1.3**

Make appropriate entries in the adjustment columns of the extended trial balance to take account of the following:

(a)    Depreciation is to be provided as follows:

Motor Vehicles - 20% per annum on cost

Fixtures and Fittings - 10% per annum reducing balance method

No depreciation is charged on assets in their year of purchase or in their year of sale.  On 12 November 1996 new fixtures and fittings costing £6,000 had been purchased.

(b)    The £150,000 was invested in the bank deposit account on 30 November 1996 at a fixed rate of interest of 6% per annum.

(c)    The general expenses figure includes the sum of £2,400 paid to a company to clean the offices of Electronics World Ltd during the period 1 April 1997 to 30 September 1997.

(d)    Stock has been valued on 31 May 1997 at £198,650.  This figure excludes a television which was damaged beyond repair and had to be scrapped (no sale proceeds).  Regis Insurance has agreed to cover the loss incurred in writing off the television.

Cost price of television - £420

Sales price of television - £630.

(e)    A cheque for £60 was issued at the beginning of May 1997 to pay for insurance cover which expired on 31 May 1997.  A bank statement showed that the cheque was paid on 20 May.  As yet no entries have been made in the books of Electronics World Ltd.

(f)    The provision for bad debts is to be adjusted to a figure representing 5% of debtors.

**Extended Trial Balance at 31 May 1997**

| DESCRIPTION | LEDGER BALANCES | | ADJUSTMENTS | |
| --- | --- | --- | --- | --- |
| | Dr. | Cr. | Dr. | Cr. |
| | £ | £ | £ | £ |
| Share Capital | | | | |
| Premises | | | | |
| Fixtures and Fittings (F and F) at cost | | | | |
| Provision for depreciation (F and F) | | | | |
| Purchases | | | | |
| Sales | | | | |
| Salaries | | | | |
| Sales returns | | | | |
| Purchases returns | | | | |
| General expenses | | | | |
| Insurance | | | | |
| Bad debts | | | | |
| Provision for bad debts | | | | |
| Debtors control account | | | | |
| Creditors control account | | | | |
| Stock at 1 June 1996 | | | | |
| Bank | | | | |
| Bank deposit account | | | | |
| Bank interest received | | | | |
| Motor vehicles (M.V.) at cost | | | | |
| Provision for depreciation (M.V.) | | | | |
| VAT (credit balance) | | | | |
| Profit and loss | | | | |
| | | | | |
| Prepayments | | | | |
| Depreciation | | | | |
| Regis Insurance | | | | |
| Closing stock - P & L | | | | |
| Closing stock - Balance sheet | | | | |
| Provision for bad debts - Adjustment | | | | |
| Bank interest owing | | | | |
| | | | | |
| | | | | |
| | | | | |
| | | | | |
| | | | | |

# SECTION 2

**Suggested time allocation: 50 minutes**

Answer each of the following questions in the space provided, as clearly and concisely as you can, or, where appropriate, circle the correct answer.

2.1  On 31 May 1997 the balances of the accounts in the Sales Ledger were listed and totalled, then compared with the balance of the Debtors Control Account. The total of the list of balances amounted to £274,189. Investigations were carried out and the following errors discovered:

(a)  a customer balance of £484 had been listed as £448;

(b)  a customer balance of £1,490 had been listed twice;

(c)  a discount of £100 allowed to a customer had been debited to the account in the Sales Ledger;

(d)  although goods of £135 (inclusive of VAT) had been returned by a customer, no entry had been made in the Sales Ledger.

Enter the appropriate adjustments in the table shown below. For each adjustment show clearly the amount involved and whether that amount is to be added or subtracted.

|  |  | £ |
|---|---|---|
| Total from listing of balances |  | 274,189 |
| Adjustment for (a) | add/subtract | . . . . . . . . . |
| Adjustment for (b) | add/subtract | . . . . . . . . . |
| Adjustment for (c) | add/subtract | . . . . . . . . . |
| Adjustment for (d) | add/subtract | . . . . . . . . . |
| Revised total to agree with Debtors Control Account |  | . . . . . . . . . |

2.2  Stock has always been valued by Electronics World Ltd on a FIFO basis and this includes the closing stock figure of £198,650 as at 31 May 1997. It has been suggested that the closing stock figure should now be recalculated on a LIFO basis.

(a)  Assuming that the prices of electronic goods have been gradually rising throughout the year would the change suggested increase profit for the year ended 31 May 1997, decrease profit or would profit remain the same?

Increase / Decrease / Remain the same

(b)  Which accounting concept states that the company should not normally change its basis for valuing stock unless it has very good reasons for doing so?

. . . . . . . . . . . . . . . . . . . . . . . . . . . . . . . . . . . . . . . . . . . . . . . . . . . . . . . . . . . . . . . . . . . . . . . . . . . . . . . . . . . . . . . . .

**2.3**    Electronics World Ltd recently arranged for a local builder to design and build an extension to the company offices.  An invoice is received from the builder on completion of the work showing two main categories of expenditure: materials (bricks, doors, windows, frames etc.) and labour.  It has been suggested that:

"Since salaries and wages are normally shown in the profit and loss account the labour cost in the invoice should be written off as an expense whilst the cost of the materials should be debited to the premises account."

(a) Do you agree with the above statement?

Yes/No

(b) Briefly explain the reason for your answer.

. . . . . . . . . . . . . . . . . . . . . . . . . . . . . . . . . . . . . . . . . . . . . . . . . . . . . . . . . . . . . .

. . . . . . . . . . . . . . . . . . . . . . . . . . . . . . . . . . . . . . . . . . . . . . . . . . . . . . . . . . . . . .

. . . . . . . . . . . . . . . . . . . . . . . . . . . . . . . . . . . . . . . . . . . . . . . . . . . . . . . . . . . . . .

. . . . . . . . . . . . . . . . . . . . . . . . . . . . . . . . . . . . . . . . . . . . . . . . . . . . . . . . . . . . . .

. . . . . . . . . . . . . . . . . . . . . . . . . . . . . . . . . . . . . . . . . . . . . . . . . . . . . . . . . . . . . .

. . . . . . . . . . . . . . . . . . . . . . . . . . . . . . . . . . . . . . . . . . . . . . . . . . . . . . . . . . . . . .

**2.4**    You are reviewing some accounting records on 10 June 1997 and discover an error in the Sales Day Book.  Although the VAT and net columns have been correctly totalled, the total column itself has been miscast.  The appropriate figures have then been transferred from the day book into the ledgers.

Preparation of which of the following, if any, would be likely to detect the error?

Bank Reconciliation Statement   /  Trial Balance   /  VAT Return   /   None of these

**2.5**     For some months Electronics World Ltd has been purchasing a range of CD racks from Arun Divan, a small local supplier, who deals exclusively with the company.  Initially invoices received from this business did not include VAT but the last invoice did have VAT, calculated at 17.5%, added to the cost of the racks.  Jackie Brown, a colleague, is confused about the regulations regarding VAT and the implications of the change.  A note is left for you by Jackie raising the following specific points:

(a)    If Electronics World Ltd is now having to pay more money for the CD racks then this must affect the profits of the company.

(b)    Arun Divan has now registered for VAT.  Since the increased money he receives from Electronics World Ltd is payable to HM Customs and Excise then his profitability must remain unchanged.

Prepare a memo to Jackie Brown covering both of the points raised.  Use the memorandum on page 219 for your answer.

# MEMO

**To:**                                         **Ref:**

**From:**                                       **Date:**

# SECTION 3

**Suggested time allocation: 55 minutes**

Note: Clearly show your workings for all tasks.

Lucy Barber previously worked full-time for a furniture manufacturing company. Approximately 2 years ago, however, she decided to set up a part-time business making and selling speaker stands for hi-fi systems. She now has an arrangement to sell exclusively to Electronics World Ltd and you have been asked to assist her in preparing her accounts for the year ended 30 April 1997.

The following information is available:

* Tools and equipment costing £3,000 were purchased for the business on 31 July 1995.

* A van costing £4,800 was purchased on 31 October 1995, again for use in the business.

* Lucy Barber rents a small workshop on a light industrial estate. The rent payable was £100 a month until 31 October 1996 but then it was increased to £120 a month and this remains as the current rate. On 30 April 1996 one month's rent was owing to the landlord.

* During Lucy Barber's first period of trading, which ended on 30 April 1996, all of the transactions were for cash. On 30 April 1996 the cash balance of the business was £4,250. On 1 May 1996 she opened a business bank account and a private bank account. The £4,250 was paid into the business account but no funds were paid at that time into the private account. From 1 May 1996 all business transactions passed through the business bank account with the exception of some cheques from Electronics World Ltd (see below).

* From 1 May 1996 sales to Electronics World Ltd were on credit as were purchases from her supplier, Johnson Materials Ltd. Cheques received from Electronics World were all paid into the business bank account apart from three which Lucy Barber paid directly into her private account.

* Throughout the year ended 30 April 1997 Lucy Barber withdrew £200 a month cash from her private account for personal spending. No other transactions passed through the account other than the three cheques paid in from Electronics World Ltd. On the 30 April 1997 the balance of the account was £600.

* During the year ended 30 April 1997 she made and sold 500 pairs of speaker stands. In determining the price charged for each pair she calculated the cost of materials used for the pair then doubled this figure.

* On 30 April 1997:
  - £4,400 was owed to the business by Electronics World Ltd;
  - £1,500 was owed by the business to Johnson Materials Ltd;
  - Materials were in stock to make 120 pairs of speaker stands.

* Lucy Barber does not have a record of the materials that were in stock on 30 April 1996.

* The van is to be depreciated at 10% per annum on cost. The tools and equipment are to be depreciated at 20% per annum on cost.

* The following is a summary made by Lucy Barber of the entries which passed through the business bank account during the year ended 30 April 1997:

| Money Received: | £ |
| --- | --- |
| Electronics World Ltd | 17,600 |
| **Money Paid Out:** | |
| Rent | 1,300 |
| Johnson Materials Ltd | 12,000 |
| Tools and Equipment | 250 |
| Electricity | 640 |
| Telephone | 560 |

**Task 3.1**

Calculate the total sales made by Lucy Barber during the year ended 30 April 1997.

**Task 3.2**

Calculate the selling price for one pair of speaker stands.

**Task 3.3**

Calculate the cost of materials used in making one pair of speaker stands.

**Task 3.4**

Calculate the total cost of goods sold during the year ended 30 April 1997 (i.e. the cost of materials used in making the sales calculated in Task 3.1).

**Task 3.5**

Calculate the cost of materials purchased by Lucy Barber during the year ended 30 April 1997.

**Task 3.6**

Calculate the stock of materials held by Lucy Barber on 30 April 1996.

**Task 3.7**

Calculate the capital invested in the business by Lucy Barber on 30 April 1996.

**Task 3.8**

Calculate the figure for rent which would be included in the calculation of profit for the year ended 30 April 1997.

# Central Assessment Tasks

## Castle Alarms

reproduced by kind permission of AAT

recommended timing 3 hours

## NOTE TO STUDENTS

This assessment was issued by AAT in December 1996 to cover the Unit 'Preparing Financial Accounts' under the pre-1998 specifications.

These tasks are still relevant to the current specifications, but students should study the structure of the 'Creative Catering' Central Assessment (page 187) for specific guidance for the revised Unit.

The Assessment is divided into three sections.

The recommended timing is as follows:

|  |  |
|---|---|
| Section 1 | 70 minutes |
| Section 2 | 30 minutes |
| Section 3 | 80 minutes |

Please note that from December 1999 the Central Assessment will be set out in two sections. The content and approach will remain the same.

# SECTION 1

**Suggested time allocation: 70 minutes**

Andrew Hallgrove is the proprietor of Castle Alarms, which specialises in supplying domestic and commercial burglar alarm systems. Although the business operates throughout the UK, the offices and warehouse are located in the north of England.

You are employed within the business to assist with the book-keeping. This is currently a manual system and consists of a general ledger, where double entry takes place, a sales ledger and a purchases ledger. The individual accounts of debtors and creditors are therefore regarded as memoranda accounts. Day books are used and totals from the various columns of these are transferred periodically into the general ledger.

At the end of the financial year on 31 October 1996, the balances were extracted from the general ledger and entered into an extended trial balance as shown on pages 226 and 227.

**Task 1.1**

Make appropriate entries in the adjustment columns of the extended trial balance to take account of the following:

(a)    Depreciation is to be provided as follows:

Motor vehicles - 20% per annum straight line method

Equipment - 10% per annum reducing balance method

(b)    The bank loan of £50,000 was taken out on 31 January 1996. The interest rate charged on the loan is fixed at 10% per annum.

(c)    In August a system invoiced at £3,400 was installed at a local restaurant. Unfortunately no money was received in payment, the restaurant closed and the owner disappeared. A decision has now been made to write off the debt.

(d)    Having written off all bad debts, the provision for bad debts is to be adjusted to 6% of remaining debtors.

(e)    At the stocktake on 31 October 1996 the stock was valued at £289,400 cost price. However, this figure includes the following:

(i)    5 systems costing £1,200 each which have now been replaced by improved models. It is thought that in order to sell them, the price of each system will have to be reduced to £1,000.

(ii)    A system costing £2,000 was damaged in the warehouse. Repairs will cost £200 before it can be used in an installation.

(f)    The business took advantage of an offer to advertise on local radio during October 1996 at a cost of £2,250. Although the invoice has now been received no entries have been made.

(g)    Rent for the business property is £2,100 payable monthly in advance. This has been the figure payable over the last 12 months and a rent review is not due at the present time.

(h)    On 30 October 1996 £5,000 cash was withdrawn from the bank for use within the business. To date no entries have been made to reflect this transaction.

(i)    A credit note received from Ashito Electronics and relating to goods returned has just been found in a pile of correspondence. The credit note, dated 20 October 1996, is for £2,900 and has not been entered in any of the books of the business.

**Task 1.2**

Extend the figures into the extended trial balance columns for profit and loss and balance sheet. Total all of these columns, transferring the balance of the profit or loss as appropriate.

The extended trial balance is set out on the next two pages.

# EXTENDED TRIAL BALANCE

| account name | ledger balances | |
|---|---|---|
| | Dr | Cr |
| | £ | £ |
| Sales | | 1,200,000 |
| Purchases | 667,820 | |
| Sales returns | 96,570 | |
| Purchases returns | | 52,790 |
| Opening stock | 301,840 | |
| Debtors control account | 189,600 | |
| Cash | 1,200 | |
| Bank | 25,300 | |
| Creditors control account | | 95,000 |
| Provision for bad debts | | 12,000 |
| Bad debts | 10,100 | |
| Discounts allowed | 6,320 | |
| Salaries | 103,030 | |
| Drawings | 26,170 | |
| Rent | 27,300 | |
| General expenses | 14,310 | |
| Capital | | 121,860 |
| VAT | | 22,600 |
| Bank loan | | 50,000 |
| Interest on bank loan | 2,500 | |
| Advertising | 11,450 | |
| Motor vehicles | 32,600 | |
| Provision for depreciation | | |
| - Motor vehicles | | 4,100 |
| Equipment | 48,860 | |
| Provision for depreciation | | |
| - Equipment | | 6,620 |
| Prepayments | | |
| Depreciation | | |
| Loan interest owing | | |
| Other accruals | | |
| Closing stock    - Profit & Loss | | |
| - Balance sheet | | |
| Provision for bad debts - adjustment | | |
| Profit | | |
| | | |
| | 1,564,970 | 1,564,970 |

name _____   date _____

| adjustments | | profit and loss | | balance sheet | |
|---|---|---|---|---|---|
| Dr | Cr | Dr | Cr | Dr | Cr |
| £ | £ | £ | £ | £ | £ |
| | | | | | |
| | | | | | |
| | | | | | |
| | | | | | |
| | | | | | |
| | | | | | |
| | | | | | |
| | | | | | |
| | | | | | |
| | | | | | |
| | | | | | |
| | | | | | |
| | | | | | |
| | | | | | |
| | | | | | |
| | | | | | |
| | | | | | |
| | | | | | |
| | | | | | |
| | | | | | |
| | | | | | |
| | | | | | |
| | | | | | |
| | | | | | |
| | | | | | |
| | | | | | |
| | | | | | |
| | | | | | |
| | | | | | |
| | | | | | |
| | | | | | |
| | | | | | |
| | | | | | |
| | | | | | |
| | | | | | |
| | | | | | |
| | | | | | |
| | | | | | |
| | | | | | |
| | | | | | |
| | | | | | |

# SECTION 2

**Suggested time allocation: 30 minutes.**

**Answer each of the following questions by writing in the space provided, as clearly and concisely as you can. Circle the correct answer where appropriate.**

2.1   Andrew Hallgrove bought a calculator costing £10 for use in the office.

Referring to the relevant accounting concept, briefly explain why the purchase would normally be treated as revenue rather than as capital expenditure, despite the fact that the calculator will probably be used for several years.

. . . . . . . . . . . . . . . . . . . . . . . . . . . . . . . . . . . . . . . . . . . . . . . . . . . . . . . . . . . . . . . . . . . .

. . . . . . . . . . . . . . . . . . . . . . . . . . . . . . . . . . . . . . . . . . . . . . . . . . . . . . . . . . . . . . . . . . . .

. . . . . . . . . . . . . . . . . . . . . . . . . . . . . . . . . . . . . . . . . . . . . . . . . . . . . . . . . . . . . . . . . . . .

. . . . . . . . . . . . . . . . . . . . . . . . . . . . . . . . . . . . . . . . . . . . . . . . . . . . . . . . . . . . . . . . . . . .

2.2   At the end of a particular quarter, Castle Alarms' VAT account showed a balance of £2,100 debit.

Explain briefly what the balance represents.

. . . . . . . . . . . . . . . . . . . . . . . . . . . . . . . . . . . . . . . . . . . . . . . . . . . . . . . . . . . . . . . . . . . .

. . . . . . . . . . . . . . . . . . . . . . . . . . . . . . . . . . . . . . . . . . . . . . . . . . . . . . . . . . . . . . . . . . . .

2.3   Andrew Hallgrove is considering leasing a car for use by one of his sales staff. He understands that leases are classified as operating leases or finance leases and the two types affect the books of a business in different ways.

Which type of lease would have to be capitalised in the books of Castle Alarms?

Finance lease / Operating lease / Both finance and operating lease / Neither finance nor operating lease

2.4   Castle Alarms makes a credit sale to Turnbull Haircare for £200 plus £35 VAT. Unfortunately, in error, the sales invoice is not entered in the sales day book.

(a) Would the error be detected by drawing up a trial balance?

Yes/No

(b) Briefly explain the reason for your answer to (a)

. . . . . . . . . . . . . . . . . . . . . . . . . . . . . . . . . . . . . . . . . . . . . . . . . . . . . . . . . . . . . . . . . . . .

. . . . . . . . . . . . . . . . . . . . . . . . . . . . . . . . . . . . . . . . . . . . . . . . . . . . . . . . . . . . . . . . . . . .

. . . . . . . . . . . . . . . . . . . . . . . . . . . . . . . . . . . . . . . . . . . . . . . . . . . . . . . . . . . . . . . . . . . .

. . . . . . . . . . . . . . . . . . . . . . . . . . . . . . . . . . . . . . . . . . . . . . . . . . . . . . . . . . . . . . . . . . . .

**2.5**    A motor vehicle which had been purchased by Castle Alarms for £10,450 was eventually sold for £3,000, when it had a net book value of £4,100.

What is the total charge to the profits of Castle Alarms with respect to the capital cost of the vehicle, during the life of the asset?

£......................

**2.6**    Castle Alarms purchases an alarm from Ace Electronics. Ace Electronics normally sells the alarm at a price of £2,400, but Castle Alarms is given a 20% trade discount. Ace Electronics charges £10 for delivery to Castle Alarms' premises. Castle Alarms puts a price on the alarm of £2,425.

What value would be placed on this particular item by Castle Alarms in valuing the stock of the business?

£.......................

**2.7**    Castle Alarms purchases 20 alarm sirens from Northern Imports Ltd. The price charged for each siren is £40 plus VAT calculated at 17.5%. A 10% cash discount is offered by Northern Imports Ltd provided that payment is made within 14 days. (NOTE: State clearly for each entry the name of the account, the amount and whether it is debit or credit).

(a)    What double entry is made in the general ledger to record the purchase (the date of payment has not yet been determined)?

. . . . . . . . . . . . . . . . . . . . . . . . . . . . . . . . . . . . . . . . . . . . . . . . . . . . . . . . . . . . . . .

. . . . . . . . . . . . . . . . . . . . . . . . . . . . . . . . . . . . . . . . . . . . . . . . . . . . . . . . . . . . . . .

. . . . . . . . . . . . . . . . . . . . . . . . . . . . . . . . . . . . . . . . . . . . . . . . . . . . . . . . . . . . . . .

(b)    What double entry is made in the general ledger to record Castle Alarms' clearing the debt by cheque whilst at the same time taking advantage of the discount offered?

. . . . . . . . . . . . . . . . . . . . . . . . . . . . . . . . . . . . . . . . . . . . . . . . . . . . . . . . . . . . . . .

. . . . . . . . . . . . . . . . . . . . . . . . . . . . . . . . . . . . . . . . . . . . . . . . . . . . . . . . . . . . . . .

. . . . . . . . . . . . . . . . . . . . . . . . . . . . . . . . . . . . . . . . . . . . . . . . . . . . . . . . . . . . . . .

**2.8**    Although Andrew Hallgrove has proved to be a good businessman, his knowledge of accounting is rather limited. In particular he does not understand how it is possible for a business to make a profit whilst at the same time the bank balance can remain static or even decrease. He has asked you to provide some guidance.

Draft a memorandum to him clearly stating how profit is measured and giving examples of why the movement of the bank balance does not necessarily reflect the profits made. Use the memorandum on the next page for your answer.

# MEMORANDUM

**To:**                                    **Ref:**

**From:**                                  **Date:**

# SECTION 3

**(Suggested time allocation: 80 minutes)**

- Andrew Hallgrove decided to open a shop selling cheap alarm systems and security equipment direct to the public. Trading was to start at the beginning of October 1996. He decided to call the shop and business 'Total Security'.

- On 1 September he opened a new bank account and paid in £50,000 of his own money as his investment in the business.

- During September he purchased shop fixtures and fittings at £22,500 and stock at £47,300. He paid £9,000 for 6 months' rent covering the period 1 September 1996 to 28 February 1997. Insurance of £480 covering the 12 months from 1 September 1996 was also paid, as were various items of general expenditure totalling £220.

- Since it was convenient to make some of the payments in cash he withdrew a lump sum from the bank.

- Unfortunately, his £50,000 investment was insufficient to cover all of the expenditure. However, he managed to negotiate a bank loan and all the monies from this were paid into the business's bank account.

- The interest rate for the bank loan was fixed at 12% per annum.

- At the end of September he had a £10,000 balance remaining in the bank account and £500 in cash.

- A summary of the business bank account for October 1996 is shown below:

|  | £ |  | £ |
|---|---|---|---|
| Balance b/d | 10,000 | To creditors | 20,250 |
| Cash banked | 22,000 | Drawings | 3,500 |
|  |  | General expenses | 500 |
|  |  | Stationery | 320 |
|  |  | Customer refund | 2,000 |
|  |  | Balance c/d | 5,430 |
|  | 32,000 |  | 32,000 |

- The cash banked all came from sales to customers. However, before banking the takings, £2,400 had been paid out as wages. The cash float at the end of October remained at £500.

- In paying his creditors he had been able to take advantage of discounts totalling £1,250. At the end of the month not all creditors had been paid, however, and he calculated that the total of the unpaid invoices amounted to £3,400.

- Depreciation is calculated on the fixtures and fittings at 20% per annum on cost.

- On 31 October 1996 a customer returned an alarm system which he had decided was not appropriate for his premises. He was given a refund by cheque.

- Unsold stock on 31 October was valued at £55,000, but this did not include the returned system. The profit margin on this type of system is 30%.

**Task 3.1**

Calculate the amount of the bank loan taken out in September, clearly showing your workings.

**Task 3.2**

List the business assets as at 30 September 1996 together with their value.  (Depreciation for September should be ignored).

**Task 3.3**

Calculate the value of the purchases made during October 1996.

**Task 3.4**

Prepare a draft statement calculating the net profit for the month ended 31 October 1996.

# Appendix

## PHOTOCOPIABLE DOCUMENTS

The following documents are reproduced in this Appendix and may be photocopied for use with the activities in this workbook. You may need to use an enlarging photocopier in some cases.

- ledger accounts

- journal page

- extended trial balance

- fixed asset register

- memorandum

Dr                                                                                      Cr

| Date | Details | Amount | Date | Details | Amount |
|------|---------|--------|------|---------|--------|
|      |         | £      |      |         | £      |
|      |         |        |      |         |        |

Dr                                                                                      Cr

| Date | Details | Amount | Date | Details | Amount |
|------|---------|--------|------|---------|--------|
|      |         | £      |      |         | £      |
|      |         |        |      |         |        |

Dr                                                                                      Cr

| Date | Details | Amount | Date | Details | Amount |
|------|---------|--------|------|---------|--------|
|      |         | £      |      |         | £      |
|      |         |        |      |         |        |

| JOURNAL | | | |
|---|---|---|---|
| **Date** | **Details** | **Dr**<br>**£** | **Cr**<br>**£** |
| | | | |
| | | | |
| | | | |
| | | | |
| | | | |

**EXTENDED TRIAL BALANCE**

name.............................

date.............................

| Description | Ledger balances | | Adjustments | | Profit and loss | | Balance sheet | |
|---|---|---|---|---|---|---|---|---|
| | Dr £ | Cr £ | Dr £ | Cr £ | Dr £ | Cr £ | Dr £ | Cr £ |
| | | | | | | | | |
| | | | | | | | | |
| | | | | | | | | |
| | | | | | | | | |
| | | | | | | | | |
| | | | | | | | | |
| | | | | | | | | |
| | | | | | | | | |
| | | | | | | | | |
| | | | | | | | | |
| | | | | | | | | |
| | | | | | | | | |
| | | | | | | | | |
| | | | | | | | | |
| Closing stock: Profit and loss | | | | | | | | |
| Closing stock: Balance sheet | | | | | | | | |
| Accruals | | | | | | | | |
| Prepayments | | | | | | | | |
| Depreciation | | | | | | | | |
| Bad debts | | | | | | | | |
| Provision for bad debts:adjustment | | | | | | | | |
| | | | | | | | | |
| Net profit/loss | | | | | | | | |

**FIXED ASSET RECORD**

No

Description

Location

Supplier

| Date | Cost (net of VAT) £ | Expected useful life | Estimated scrap value £ | Depreciation method SL or RB | Percentage per annum | Depreciation for year £ | Provision for dep'n £ | Net book value £ | Disposal proceeds (net of VAT) £ | Profit/loss on sale £ |
|---|---|---|---|---|---|---|---|---|---|---|
| | | | | | | | | | | |
| | | | | | | | | | | |
| | | | | | | | | | | |
| | | | | | | | | | | |
| | | | | | | | | | | |

# MEMORANDUM

**To:**

**From:**

**Subject:**                                           **Date:**